W9-CUQ-486

Teacher's Resource Masters

VOLUME 1

Topics 1–8

Interactive Math Stories
Home-School Connection Letters
Math and Science Activities
Daily Common Core Review
Reteach to Build Understanding
Center Games
Fluency Practice/Assessment

SCOTT FORESMAN · ADDISON WESLEY

Glenview, Illinois • Boston, Massachusetts • Chandler, Arizona • Hoboken, New Jersey

ISBN-13: 978-0-328-82755-8
ISBN-10: 0-328-82755-X
3 4 5 6 7 8 9 10 11 V0N4 19 18 17 16 15

Grade K
Volume 1: Topics 1–8

Topic 1   **Numbers 0 to 5**

Topic 1 Interactive Math Story

Topic 1 Home-School Connection (English and Spanish)

Topic 2   **Compare Numbers 0 to 5**

Topic 2 Interactive Math Story

Topic 2 Home-School Connection (English and Spanish)

Topic 3   **Numbers 6 to 10**

Topic 3 Interactive Math Story

Topic 3 Home-School Connection (English and Spanish)

Topic 4   **Compare Numbers 0 to 10**

Topic 4 Interactive Math Story

Topic 4 Home-School Connection (English and Spanish)

Topic 5 Classify and Count Data

Topic 6 Understand Addition

Topic 7 Understand Subtraction

Topic 8 More Addition and Subtraction

This book belongs to:

Count the Eggs

Written by Dale Dycus
Illustrated by Chris Lensch

Mama bird is on her nest.

Help Mama bird count her eggs.

Topic 1 **1**

---

fold down

Mama bird counts 1, 2, 3, 4, _____ eggs.

Topic 1 **4**

Mama bird counts
1, 2, ____ eggs.

fold up

Mama bird counts
1, 2, 3, ____ eggs.

Name _____

Numbers 0 to 5

Topic 1 Standards

K.CC.A.3, K.CC.B.4, K.CC.B.4a, K.CC.B.4b, K.CC.B.4c, K.CC.B.5, K.OA.A.3
See the front of the Student's Edition for complete standards.

Dear Family,

Your child is learning about numbers from 1 to 5. In this topic, he or she will learn to recognize numbers 1 through 5 in different arrangements, and then learn how to write them.

Number Arrangements
Counting tells how many are in a set, regardless of the arrangement or order of the objects.

The same number is shown in each arrangement.

Try this activity with your child to practice counting 1 to 5 objects in different arrangements.

Arrange the Objects

Place 10 small objects on a table such as pennies or buttons. Say a number from 3 to 5 and have your child arrange the objects in two different ways to show that number. For example, he or she can show the number 4 as a row, a column, or in a square pattern.

Observe Your Child

Focus on Mathematical Practice 2:
Reason abstractly and quantitatively.

Help your child become proficient with Mathematical Practice 2. Change the arrangement of the objects and ask if the number of objects has changed. Ask your child to explain why the number of objects stays the same regardless of their arrangement.

Nombre _____

Números del 0 al 5

Estándares del Tema 1

K.CNC.A.3, K.CNC.B.4, K.CNC.B.4a, K.CNC.B.4b, K.CNC.B.4c, K.CNC.B.5, K.OA.A.3
Los estándares completos se encuentran en las páginas preliminares del
Libro del estudiante.

Estimada familia:

Su niño(a) está aprendiendo sobre los números del 1 al 5. En este tema, aprenderá a identificar los números del 1 al 5 en diferentes ordenaciones y luego aprenderá a escribirlos.

Ordenaciones de números

El conteo indica cuántos hay en un conjunto, sin importar la ordenación o el orden de los objetos.

Cada ordenación muestra el mismo número.

Intente realizar esta actividad con su niño(a) para practicar el conteo de objetos del 1 al 5 en diferentes ordenaciones.

Ordenar los objetos

Coloque 10 objetos pequeños sobre una mesa, como monedas de 1¢ o botones. Diga un número del 3 al 5 y pida a su niño(a) que ordene los objetos de dos maneras diferentes para mostrar ese número. Por ejemplo, él o ella puede mostrar el número 4 como una fila, una columna o en un patrón cuadrado.

Observe a su niño(a)

Enfoque en la Práctica matemática 2:
Razonar de manera abstracta y cuantitativa.

Ayude a su niño(a) a adquirir competencia en la Práctica matemática 2. Cambie la ordenación de los objetos y pregúntele si el número de objetos ha cambiado. Pídale que explique por qué el número de objetos permanece igual sin importar su ordenación.

Name _____

Rain

_____
- - - - - - - - -
_____

_____
- - - - - - - - -
_____

Directions Say: _Did you know that when it rains, and the sun comes out, a rainbow may be seen in the sky? Rainbows have the colors: red, orange, yellow, green, blue, indigo, and violet._ Have students: ★ count the number of raindrops, and then write the number to tell how many; ② color and count the number of raindrops, and then write the number to tell how many. **Extension** Have students draw a picture of a cloud and 0 to 5 raindrops. Then have them write the number to tell how many.

Name _____

Clothes for Different Weather

 1

_____
- - - - - - - - -
_____

 2

_____
- - - - - - - - -
_____

Directions Say: *Did you know that the way people dress depends on the weather? Many people wear heavy clothes in the winter to keep warm, and light clothes in the summer to stay cool. Some people wear special clothes when it rains to stay dry.* Have students circle and count the clothes people wear in the: ⭐ summer, and then write the number to tell how many; ❷ winter, and then write the number to tell how many. Have students use objects, words, or a method of their choice to explain why people wear more clothes in the winter. **Extension** Have students draw pictures of clothes people can wear when it rains, and then write the number to tell how many. Then have them use objects, words, or a method of their choice to explain why some people wear special clothes when it rains.

Math and Science Activity ⬤ 1·11

Name _____

 1

Ⓐ

Ⓑ

Ⓒ

Ⓓ

2

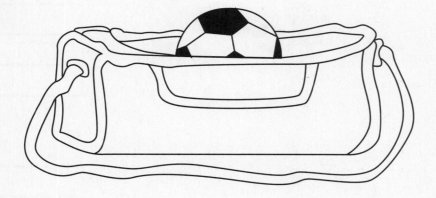

Directions Have students: ⭐ mark the picture that shows 3 teddy bears; **2** color the boxes to show how many soccer balls are in the bag.

D 1·1

Name _____

  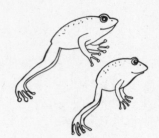 

   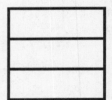

Directions Say: ⭐ *Look at the hamsters. Let's* **count** *them together: 1, 2, 3. Draw a circle around the group with 2 frogs;* 🍎 *How many mice are there? Color 1 box to show that there is 1 mouse;* 🐟 *How many dogs are there? Color the boxes to show how many;* ♥ *How many rabbits are there? Color the boxes to show how many.* **On the Back!** *Have students draw 1, 2, or 3 counters, and then tell how many they drew.*

R 1·1

Name _____

1

Ⓐ

Ⓒ

Ⓑ

Ⓓ

2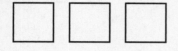

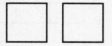

Directions Have students: **1** mark the picture that shows 2 stars; **2** draw a circle around the picture with the same number of boxes as the number of boxes at the top.

Name _____

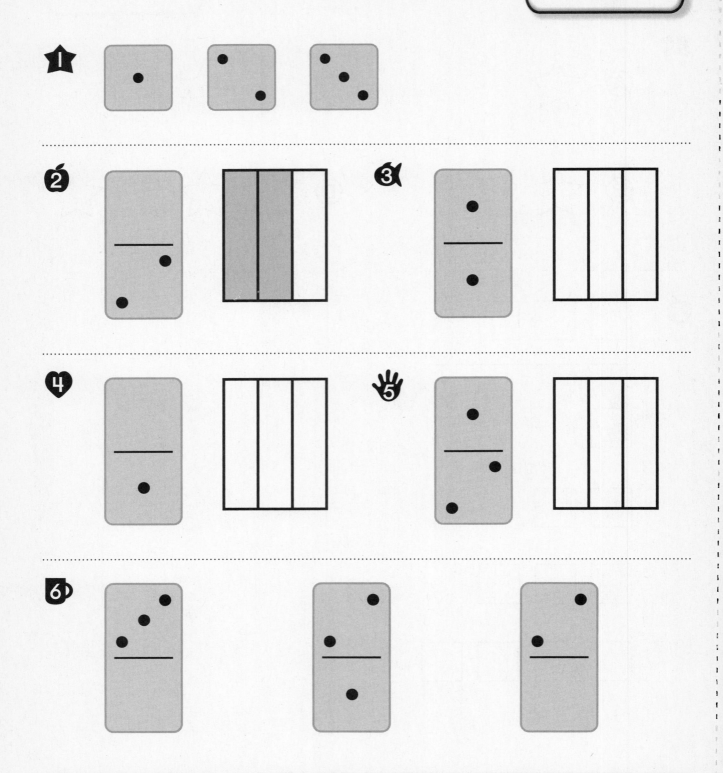

Directions Say: ⭐ *Look at the dot cubes. Let's count the dots on each dot cube. Draw a circle around the cube with* **three** *dots;* ❷ *Look at the dot tile. How many dots are there? Color the boxes to show 2 dots. This is one way to show 2;* ❸ *This dot tile has dots on both sides. How many dots are there? Color the boxes to show 2 dots. This is a different way to show 2.* Have students: ❹ *and* ✋ *count the dots, and then color the boxes to show how many;* ❻ *draw a circle around the dot tiles with 3 dots.* **On the Back!** Have students draw a group of 3 counters, and then draw another group of 3 counters in a different way.

Cover Three

Partner Talk

Share your thinking while you work.

 **Start** Put 1 1 1 2 2 2 3 3 3 in a 🛍.

Get 6 red squares.

Get 6 blue squares.

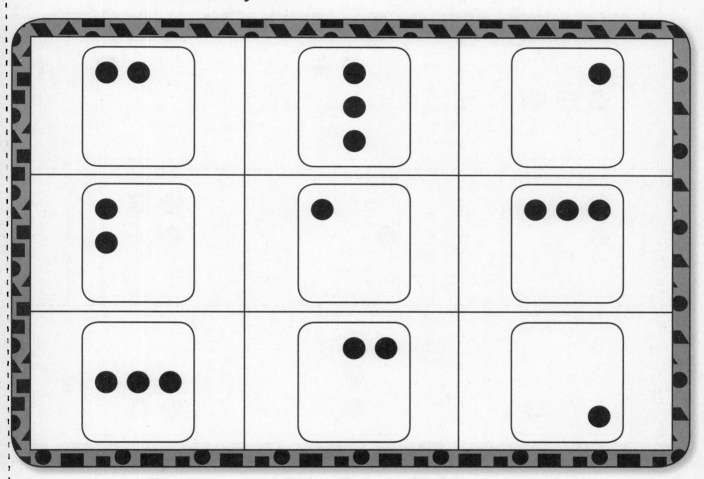

To win, get: ■ ■ ■ or ■ or ■ or

Materials   Number tiles 1, 1, 1, 2, 2, 2, 3, 3, and 3, paper bag, 6 red squares, 6 blue squares

Oral Directions   **TRY** Give 6 red squares to one player. Give 6 blue squares to the other player. Take turns. Pick a tile. Look at the game board. Point to that number of dots. Use a square to cover that group of dots. Put the tile aside. Take turns until one player wins. You can see the ways to win below the game board.

TRY AGAIN If you have time, play again!

Cover Three

Start 👥 Put | 1 | | 1 | | 1 | | 2 | | 2 | | 2 | | 3 | | 3 | | 3 | in a 🛍.

Get 6 red squares.
Get 6 blue squares.

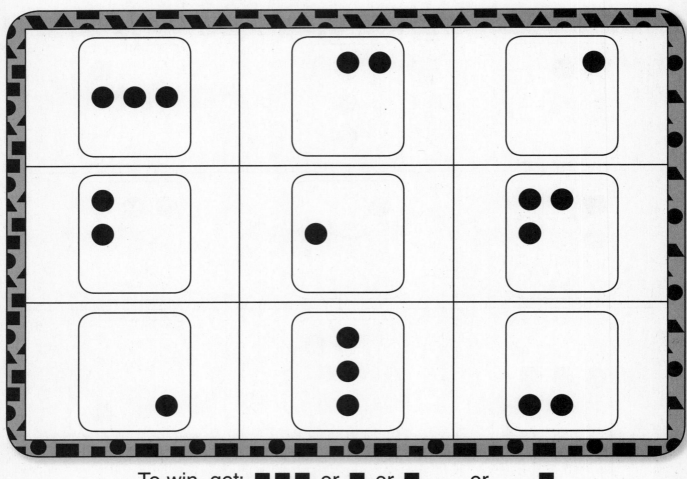

To win, get: ■ ■ ■ or ■ or ■ or ■
                    ■   ■ ■   ■   ■
                    ■

Materials	Number tiles 1, 1, 1, 2, 2, 2, 3, 3, and 3, paper bag, 6 red squares, 6 blue squares
Oral Directions	**TRY** Give 6 red squares to one player. Give 6 blue squares to the other player. Take turns. Point to a picture on the game board. Then pick a tile. If the number on the tile is the same as the number of dots in the picture, cover your picture with a square. If not, your turn is over. Put the tile back in the bag. Take turns until one player wins. You can see the ways to win below the game board.
	TRY AGAIN If you have time, play again! This time, before you pick a tile, name all of the numbers in the bag that will not match your picture.

Name _____

Ⓐ   1
Ⓑ   2
Ⓒ   3
Ⓓ   4

2

3

Directions Have students: ⭐ mark the number that tells how many animals; ❷ and ❸ count the animals, and then color the boxes to show how many.

Name _____

Directions Say: ⭐ *Look at the numbers. Let's point to each **number** and say the name: one, two, three. Write the numbers;* 🍎 *Count the rockets, and then color the boxes to show how many. Now write the number two;* 🔷 *Count the planets, and then color the boxes to show how many. Write the number that tells how many.* ❤️ *and* ✋ *Count the objects, and then practice writing the numbers that tell how many.* **On the Back!** Have students draw groups of 1, 2, and 3 objects, and then write the numbers that tell how many.

Helping Hands

Start 👫 Look at the picture.

Materials	None
Oral Directions	**TRY** Look at the picture. Talk about what you see. Then, take turns. Point to some birds. Ask your partner to say that number. Use your finger to trace that number on the beach.
	TRY AGAIN If you have time, play again! This time, point to some clouds. Say and trace that number.

Helping Hands

Partner Talk
Share your thinking while you work.

Start 👫 Look at the picture.

Materials None

Oral Directions **TRY** Look at the picture. Talk about what you see. Then, take turns. Use your finger to trace a number on the beach. Ask your partner to say that number. Have your partner point to that number of birds or clouds.

TRY AGAIN If you have time, play again! Or, trace two numbers to make 3. Tell why those two numbers make 3.

Center Game ★★ **1·3**

Copyright © Pearson Education, Inc., or its affiliates. All Rights Reserved. **K**

1

Ⓐ 4
Ⓑ 3
Ⓒ 2
Ⓓ 1

2

_____

- - - - - - - - - - - - - - -

_____

3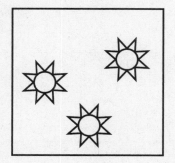

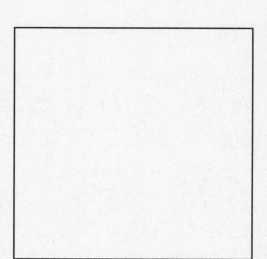

Directions Have students: **1** mark the number that tells how many moons; **2** count the stars, and then practice writing the number that tells how many; **3** count the suns, and then draw the same number of counters in the box to show how many.

Name _____

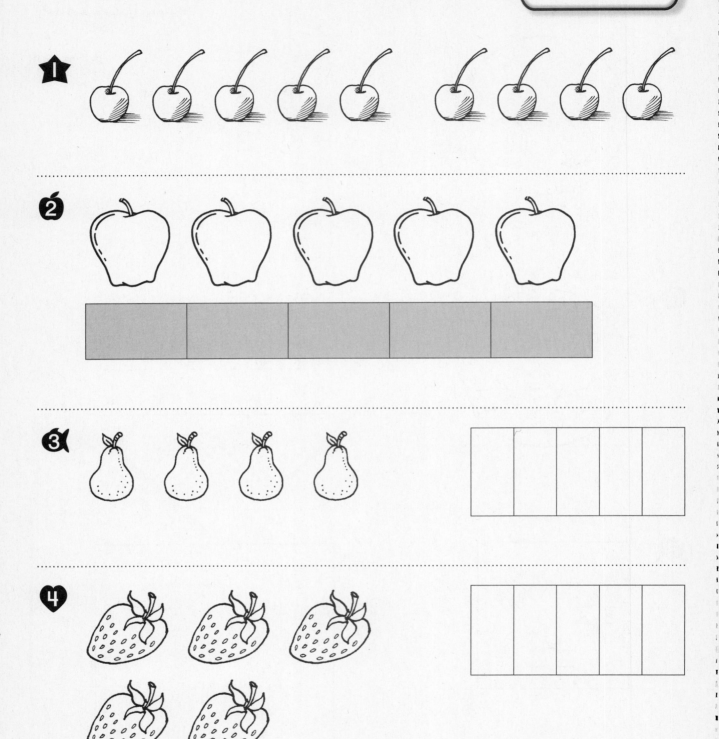

Directions Say: ❶ *Look at the two groups of cherries. Let's count how many cherries are in each group. Draw a circle around the group that has* **four** *cherries;* ❷ *How many apples are there? Color the boxes to show 5 apples;* ❸ *How many pears are there? Color the boxes to show how many;* ❹ *How many strawberries are there? Color the boxes to show how many.* **On the Back!** *Have students draw 4 or 5 counters, and then tell how many they drew.*

R 1·4

Look and See

Start 👫 Get 5 red squares. Get 4 blue squares.

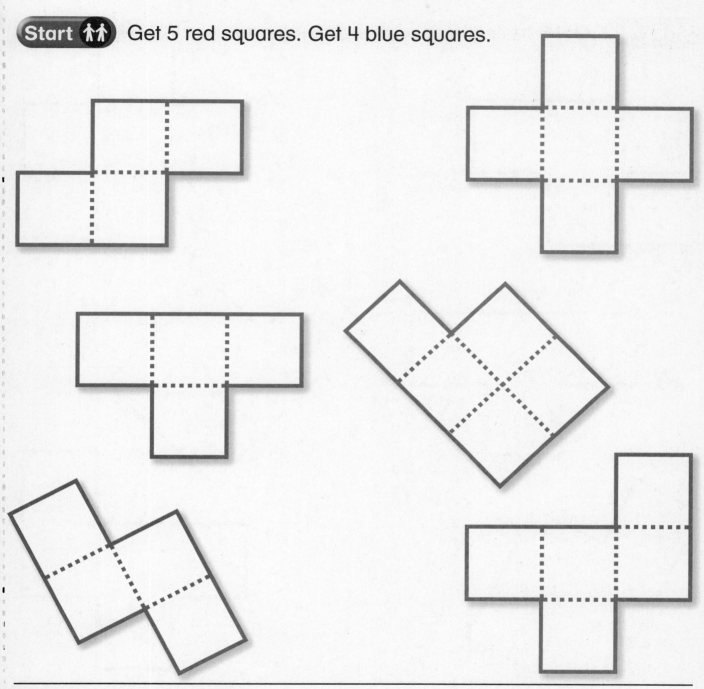

Materials	5 red squares, 4 blue squares

Oral Directions

TRY Take turns. Choose a puzzle. Use only red squares to fill that puzzle. Count the squares. Tell your partner how many squares you used to fill the puzzle. Remove the squares. Take turns until you fill every puzzle.

TRY AGAIN If you have time, fill each puzzle again. This time, use some red squares and some blue squares to fill each puzzle.

Look and See

Start 👫 Get 5 red squares. Get 4 blue squares.

Materials	5 red squares, 4 blue squares
Oral Directions	**TRY** Take turns. Choose a puzzle. Use only red squares to fill that puzzle. Count the squares. Ask your partner to count the squares in a different way. Remove the squares. Take turns until you fill every puzzle.
	TRY AGAIN If you have time, fill each puzzle again. This time, use some red squares and some blue squares. Then, make your own design with 4 squares or 5 squares. Ask your partner to count the squares in your design.

1

(A) 2

(B) 3

(C) 4

(D) 5

2

Directions Have students: **1** mark the number that tells how many boats; **2** draw a circle around the group that has 5 counters.

D 1·5

Name _____

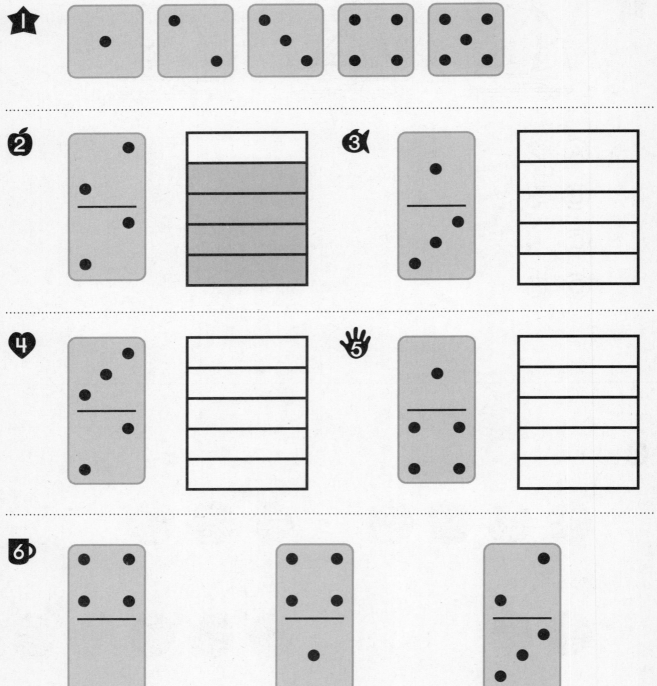

Directions Say: ⭐ *Look at the dot cubes. Let's count the dots on each cube together. Draw a circle around the cube with* ***five*** *dots;* 🍎 *Look at the dot tile. How many dots are there? Color the boxes to show 4 dots. This is one way to show 4;* 🐦 *How many dots are there? Color the boxes to show how many. This is a different way to show 4.* Have students: ❤️ and ✋ *count the dots, and then color the boxes to show how many;* ☕ *draw a circle around the dot tiles with 5 dots.* **On the Back!** Have students draw 4 counters, and then draw another group of 4 counters in a different way.

Play a Game

 Get 2 red squares.

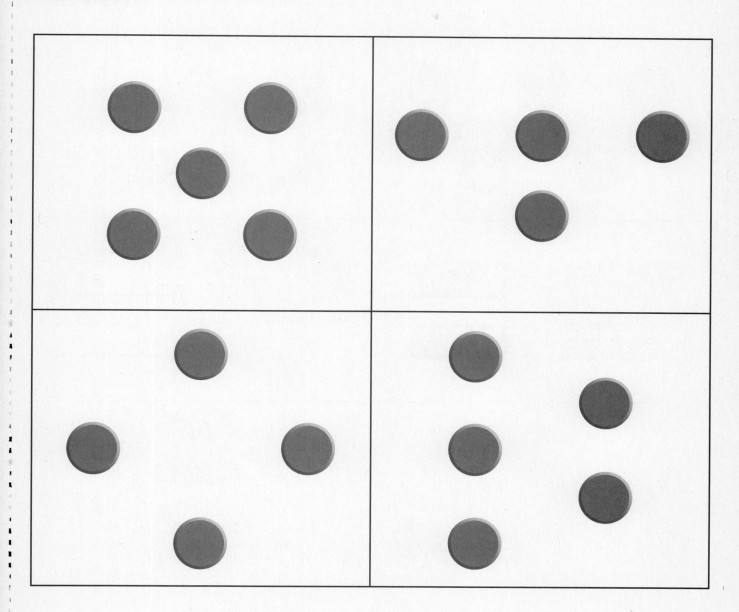

Materials   2 red squares

Oral Directions   **TRY** Player 1 chooses two boxes on the page and puts a red square in each box. Player 2 looks at the objects in each box and says if the numbers of objects in both boxes match. Count the number of objects in each box to make sure the answer is correct. Then switch roles and play again.

TRY AGAIN If you have time, play again!

Play a Game

Start 👥 Get 2 red squares.

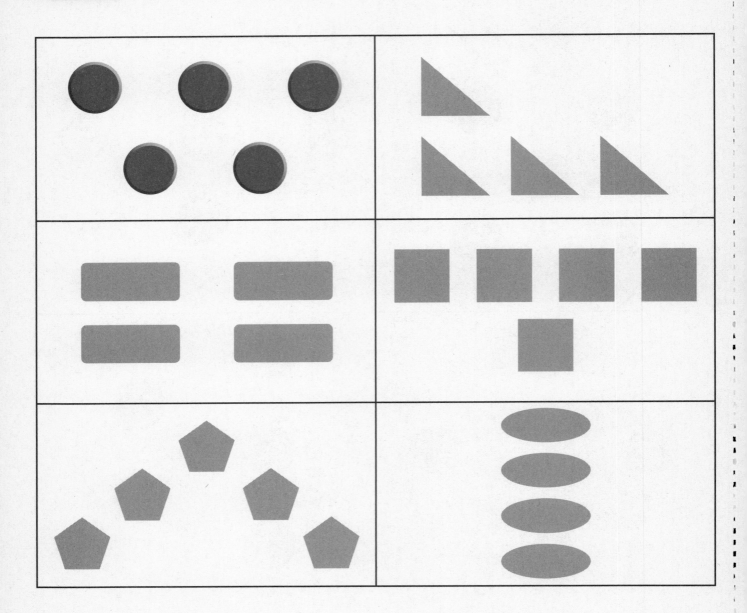

Materials 2 red squares

Oral Directions **TRY** Player 1 chooses two boxes and puts a red square in each box. Player 2 looks at the objects in each box and says if the number of objects match in both boxes. Count the number of objects in each box to make sure that the answer is correct. Then switch roles and play again.

TRY AGAIN If you have time, play again!

Name _____

★1

Ⓐ

Ⓑ

Ⓒ

Ⓓ

🍎2

1   2   3   4

Ⓐ   Ⓑ   Ⓒ   Ⓓ

★3

 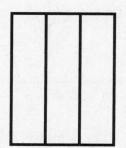

Directions Have students: ★1 mark the picture that shows I fork; 🍎2 mark the number that tells how many books; ★3 count the ducks, and then color the boxes to show how many.

D 1·6

Name _____

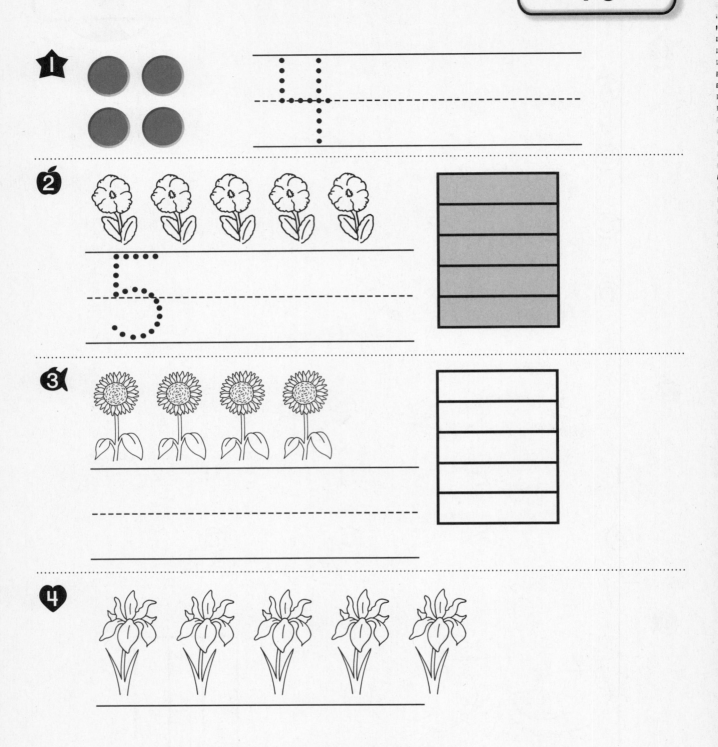

Directions Say: ⭐ *Look at the counters. Let's count them together: 1, 2, 3, 4. Practice writing the* **number** *4;* ❷ *How many flowers are there? Color the boxes to show 5 flowers. Practice writing the number 5;* ❸ *How many flowers are there? Color the boxes to show how many, and then practice writing the number;* ❹ *Count the flowers, and then practice writing the number that tells how many.* **On the Back!** *Have students draw groups of 4 and 5 objects, and then write the numbers that tell how many.*

Helping Hands

Start 👫 Put ① 2 3 4 5 in a 🛍.

Materials	Number tiles 1–5, a bag for the tiles
Oral Directions	**TRY** Put the number tiles with 1, 2, 3, 4, and 5 in the bag. Take turns. Pick a tile. Point to that number of birds. Say your number. Use your finger to trace it on the beach. Set the tile aside. Take turns until the bag is empty.
	TRY AGAIN If you have time, play again! This time point to some clouds after you pick a tile. Say and trace that number.

Helping Hands

Start 👫 Put 1 2 3 4 5 in a 🛍.

Materials	Number tiles 1–5, a bag for the tiles
Oral Directions	**TRY** Put number tiles with 1, 2, 3, 4, and 5 in the bag. Take turns. Pick a tile. Say that number. Use your finger to trace that number on the beach. Ask your partner to point to that number of birds or clouds. Set the tile aside. Take turns until the bag is empty. **TRY AGAIN** If you have time, play again! Or, show and explain ways to make 4 by tracing two numbers. Then, show and explain ways to make 5 by tracing two numbers.

Name _____

 1

Ⓐ

Ⓑ

Ⓒ

Ⓓ

 2

Ⓐ 0   Ⓒ 2

Ⓑ 1   Ⓓ 3

 3

_____

- - - - - - - - - - - - - - - -

_____

Directions Have students: **1** mark the picture that shows 4 zebras; **2** mark the number that tells how many stars; **3** count the counters, and then practice writing the number that tells how many.

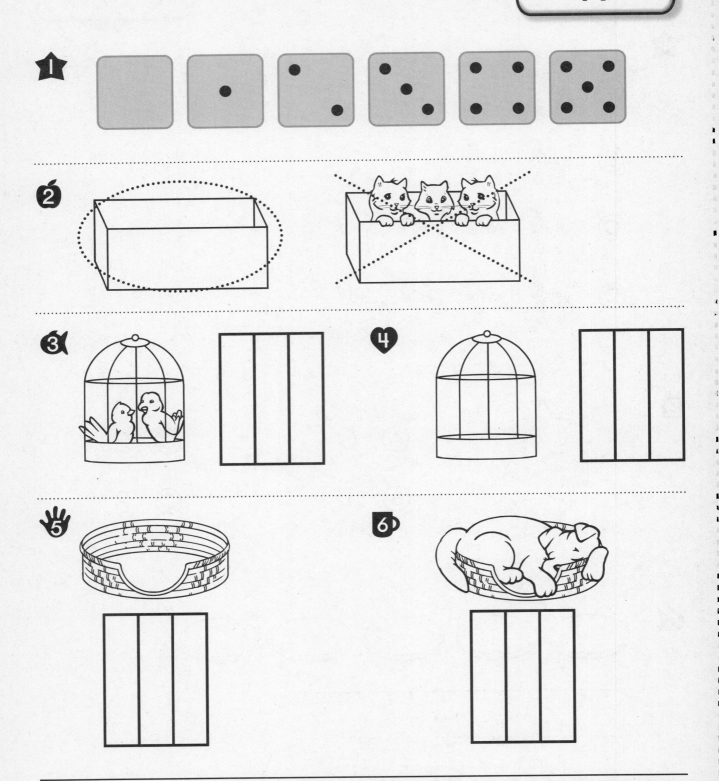

Directions Say: ⭐ *Look at the dot cubes. Let's count the dots on each dot cube together. Draw a circle around the cube with **zero** dots;* ② *Look at the boxes. How many kittens are in the first box? How many kittens are in the other box? Draw a circle around the box that shows 0 kittens. Mark an X on the box that does NOT show 0 kittens;* ③ *How many birds are there? Color the boxes to show how many;* ④ *How many birds are there? How many boxes do you color to show 0?* ✋ *and* ☕ *Have students count the puppies in the bed, and then color the boxes to show how many.* **On the Back!** *Have students draw a plate with 2 oranges, and then draw another plate with 0 oranges.*

Cover Three

 Put 0 0 0 1 1 1 2 2 3 3 4 in a .

Get 6 red squares.
Get 6 blue squares.

To win, get: ■ ■ ■ or ■ or ■ or ■
                    ■   ■   ■
                    ■   ■   ■

Materials	Number tiles 0, 0, 1, 1, 2, 2, 3, 3, and 4, paper bag, 6 red squares, 6 blue squares
Oral Directions	**TRY** Give 6 red squares to one player. Give 6 blue squares to the other player. Take turns. Pick a tile. Look at the game board. Point to that number of people in a car. Use a square to cover that car. Put the tile aside. Take turns until one player wins. You can see the ways to win below the game board.
	TRY AGAIN If you have time, play again!

Cover Three

Partner Talk

Share your thinking while you work.

Start 👥 Put 0 0 1 1 2 2 3 3 4 in a 🛍.

Get 6 red squares.
Get 6 blue squares.

To win, get: ■ ■ ■ or ■ or ■ or ■

Materials   Number tiles 0, 0, 1, 1, 2, 2, 3, 3, and 4, paper bag, 6 red squares, 6 blue squares

Oral Directions   **TRY** Give 6 red squares to one player. Give 6 blue squares to the other player. Take turns. Point to a picture on the game board. Then pick a tile. If the number on the tile is the same as the number of people in the picture, cover your picture with a square. If not, your turn is over. Put the tile back in the bag. Take turns until one player wins. You can see the ways to win below the game board.

TRY AGAIN If you have time, play again! This time, before you pick a tile, name all of the numbers in the bag that will NOT match your picture.

Center Game ★★ **1·7**

Name _____

Ⓐ

Ⓑ

Ⓒ

Ⓓ

2

Directions Have students: ⭐ mark the picture that shows 5 counters; 🍎 count the birds, and then color the boxes to show how many.

Name _____

Directions Say: ⭐ *Look at the circles. Let's count the stars inside each circle. Mark an X on the picture that shows there are* **none**; 🍎 *How many flowers are in the flower pot? Color the boxes to show 0 flowers, and then practice writing the number zero;* 🐟 *How many fish are in the bowl? Color the boxes to show how many, and then practice writing the number that tells how many;* ❤️ *How many marbles are in the jar? Practice writing the number that tells how many.*
On the Back! Have students draw a plate with 2 crackers, draw another plate with 0 crackers, and then practice writing the numbers that tell how many.

Listen and Learn

 Start  Snap your fingers.
Count 5 snaps.

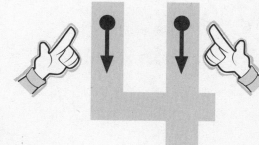

Materials   None

Oral Directions   **TRY** Practice snapping your fingers. Then take turns. Point to a number. Snap your fingers that number of times while your partner listens. Ask your partner to say your number, and then finger trace your number. Take turns until you snap each number.

TRY AGAIN If you have time, trace any number. Ask your partner to snap that number. Talk about how 0 is different from the other numbers.

Center Game ★ 1·8

Listen and Learn

Partner Talk
Share your thinking while you work.

Start 👫 Snap your fingers.
Count 5 snaps.

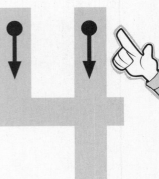

Materials   None

**Oral
Directions**   **TRY** Practice snapping your fingers. Then take turns. Point to a number. Say that number. Snap that
number. Ask your partner to listen and to finger trace your number. Take turns until you snap each number.

TRY AGAIN If you have time, snap a number. Ask your partner to finger trace that number. Talk about
the numbers you can trace without taking your finger off the page.

Name _____

★1

Ⓐ 2

Ⓑ 3

Ⓒ 4

Ⓓ 5

2

_____

Ⓐ ◯

Ⓑ ◯ ◯

Ⓒ ◯ ◯ ◯

Ⓓ ◯ ◯ ◯ ◯

3

Directions Have students: **★1** mark the number that tells how many horses; **2** mark the picture that shows the same number of counters as the number of counters at the top; **3** count the leaves on the tree, and then practice writing the number that tells how many.

D 1·9

Name _____

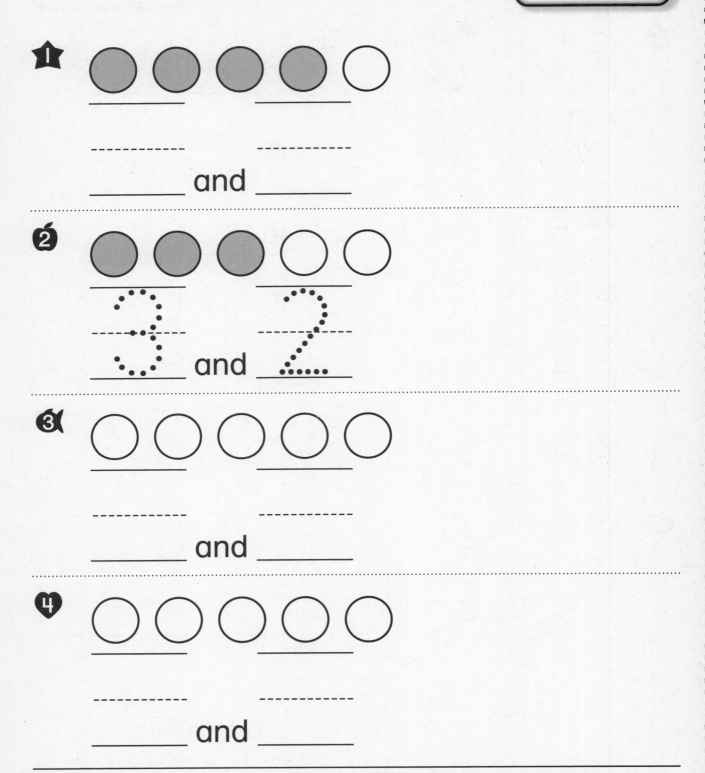

❶ _____ and _____

❷ 3 and 2

❸ _____ and _____

❹ _____ and _____

Directions Say: ❶ *The **whole** tells how many in all. Let's count the counters: 1, 2, 3, 4, 5. How many counters, or* **parts,** *are gray? How many are white? Write the numbers that tell the parts. This shows one way to make 5;* ❷ *How many counters are there in all? How many counters are gray? How many counters are white? Write the numbers that tell the parts. This shows another way to make 5;* ❸ *and* ❹ *Use two different colors. Color the counters to show a different way to make 5, and then write the numbers that tell the parts.* **On the Back!** Have students use two different colors to draw 5 counters that show a different way to make 5. Then have them write the numbers.

1

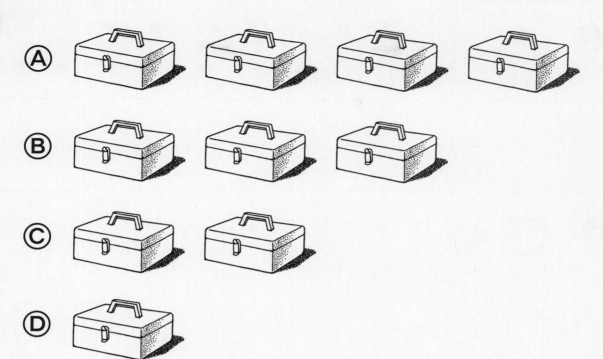

(A)

(B)

(C)

(D)

 2

Directions Have students: **1** mark the picture that shows 2 cases; **2** count the bears, and then draw the same number of counters.

Name _____

⭐ 1

⎯⎯⎯ ⎯⎯⎯ ⎯⎯⎯ ⎯⎯⎯ ⎯⎯⎯ ⎯⎯⎯

- - - - - - - - - - - - - - - - - - - - - - - - - - - - - -

🍎 2

0   1   - - - - -   - - - - -   - - - - -

🗲 3

⎯⎯⎯ ⎯⎯⎯ ⎯⎯⎯ ⎯⎯⎯ ⎯⎯⎯ ⎯⎯⎯

- - - - - - - - - - - - - - - - - - - - - - - - - - - - - -

Directions ⭐ Say: *Look at the dot tiles. Let's count the dots on each tile. Write the numbers in* **order** *to tell how many dots on each tile.* 🍎 *Point to the empty rectangle.* Say: *How many counters are there? Write the number that tells how many.* Have students draw counters to show the numbers 1 to 4, and then write the numbers in order. 🗲 Have students count the beetles in each group, write the numbers in order, and then draw a circle around the number that comes just after 4 when counting. **On the Back!** Have students practice writing the numbers 0 to 5 in order, and then draw a circle around the number that comes just before 1 when counting.

1

Ⓐ    Ⓑ

Ⓒ    Ⓓ

2

Ⓐ   5

Ⓑ   2

Ⓒ   3

Ⓓ   4

3

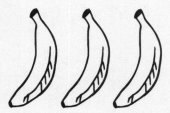

Directions Have students: **1** mark the picture that shows 2 apples; **2** mark the picture that shows the number 4; **3** count the bananas, and then color the boxes to show how many.

⭐1 _____ _____ _____ _____ _____ _____

- - - - - - -   - - - - - - -   - - - - - - -   - - - - - - -   - - - - - - -

_____ _____ _____ _____ _____

🍎2

3

3

4

Directions ⭐ Say: *Let's **count** from 0 to 5: 1, 2, 3, 4, 5. Write the numbers, and then circle the number zero.* Have students make a math argument about how many animals are in each row, and then write the number. Have them use objects, words, or a method of their choice to explain their arguments and tell why they are correct. Say: ❷ *How many cats are there?* ❸ *How many squirrels are there?* ❹ *How many moose are there?* **On the Back!** Have students draw a group of 4 objects, and then write the number that tells how many. Have them use objects, words, or a method of their choice to explain how they know their answer is correct.

This book belongs to:

I am Anna

Written by Diane Brown   Illustrated by Rémy Simard

h Ii Jj Kk Ll Mm Nn Oo Pp Qq

I see hooks.

I see coats.

I see more ____ .

fold down

I see green blocks.

I see blue blocks.

I see yellow blocks.

I see fewer ____ .

I see hats.

I see shoes.

I see fewer _____ .

fold up

I see mops.

I see brooms.

I see more _____ .

Name _____

Compare Numbers 0 to 5

Topic 2 Standards
K.CC.C.6, K.CC.C.7
See the front of the Student's Edition for complete standards.

Dear Family,

Your child is learning to compare numbers from 0 to 5. In this topic, he or she will learn to compare groups of objects to identify if one group is greater in number, less in number, or equal in number to another group.

Comparing Groups
Match each object from one group with an object from a second group to decide which group is greater in number, less in number, or if the groups have the same number of objects.

Here is an activity you can do with your child to practice comparing numbers to 5.

more

less

same as

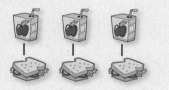

Greater Than or Less Than

Make a set of number cards from 1 to 4. Gather 5 buttons or pennies. Mix up the number cards and place them facedown on a table. Have your child choose 1 card and read the number aloud. Then you say "greater than" or "less than." Ask your child to show a group of objects that is greater in number or less in number. For example, if the number 4 card is chosen and you say "less than," your child makes a group with 1, 2 or 3 buttons. Switch roles and continue the game.

Observe Your Child

Focus on Mathematical Practice 3:
Construct viable arguments and critique the reasoning of others.

Help your child become proficient with Mathematical Practice 3. During one of your turns, purposely show the incorrect number of objects. Ask your child to explain why you are wrong and how he or she knows.

Comparar los números del 0 al 5

Estándares del Tema 2

K.CNC.C.6, K.CNC.C.7
Los estándares completos se encuentran en las páginas preliminares del
Libro del estudiante.

Estimada familia:

Su niño(a) está aprendiendo a comparar los números del 0 al 5. En este tema, aprenderá a comparar grupos de objetos para identificar si un grupo tiene más, menos o el mismo número de objetos que otro grupo.

Comparar grupos

Empareja cada objeto de un grupo con un objeto de un segundo grupo para decidir qué grupo tiene más, menos o si los grupos tienen el mismo número de objetos.

más

menos

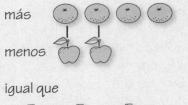

igual que

Esta es una actividad que puede hacer con su niño(a) para practicar la comparación de los números hasta el 5.

Mayor que o menor que

Haga un conjunto de tarjetas numéricas del 1 al 4. Reúna 5 botones o monedas de 1¢. Mezcle las tarjetas numéricas y póngalas boca abajo sobre una mesa. Pida a su niño(a) que escoja 1 tarjeta y lea el número en voz alta. Luego, diga: "mayor que" o "menor que". Pídale a su niño(a) que muestre un grupo de objetos que sea mayor o menor. Por ejemplo, si escoge la tarjeta número 4 y usted dice "menor que", su niño(a) deberá formar un grupo con 1, 2 o 3 botones. Intercambien los papeles y sigan jugando.

Observe a su niño(a)

Enfoque en la Práctica matemática 3:

Construir argumentos viables y evaluar el razonamiento de otros.

Ayude a su niño(a) a adquirir competencia en la Práctica matemática 3. En uno de sus turnos, muestre a propósito el número incorrecto de objetos. Pida a su niño(a) que explique por qué no tiene razón y cómo lo sabe.

Name _____

Snow Rollers

Directions Say: *Did you know that strong winds that blow across a flat, snow-covered field can form a hollow snow ball?
This type of snow ball is called a* snow roller. Have students: and draw lines between the two groups to match the
snow rollers from one group to the other. Then have them draw a circle around the groups if they are equal in number, or
mark an X on the groups if they are NOT equal in number. **Extension** Have students draw a group of snow rollers. Then
have them draw another group of snow rollers that is NOT equal to the first group.

Math and Science Activity **2·1**

Name _____

Rainbows

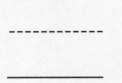

_____

- - - - - - - - - - - - - - - - -

_____

_____

- - - - - - - - - - - - - - - - -

_____

_____

- - - - - - - - - - - - - - - - -

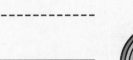

_____

_____

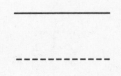

_____

- - - - - - - - - - - - - - - - -

Directions Say: *Did you know that a rainbow is really a full circle of seven colors? The lower the sun is to the horizon, the more of the circle you can see. Most people only see the arc, or bow, of a rainbow in sunny or rainy weather.*
⭐ and ❷ Have students count the stickers, and then write the numbers to tell how many. Have them draw a circle around the number that is greater than the other number and mark an X on the number that is less than the other number, or draw a circle around both numbers if they are equal. **Extension** Have students draw a group of clouds, and then draw a group of raindrops that is less in number than the group of clouds. Then have them write the number to tell how many in each group.

Ⓐ

Ⓑ

Ⓒ

Ⓓ

🍎 **2**

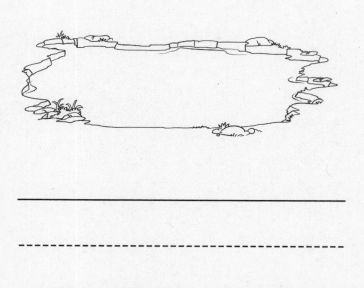

_____

- -

_____

Directions Have students: ⭐ mark the picture that shows 5 cows; 🍎 count the ducks in the pond, and then practice writing the number that tells how many.

Name _____

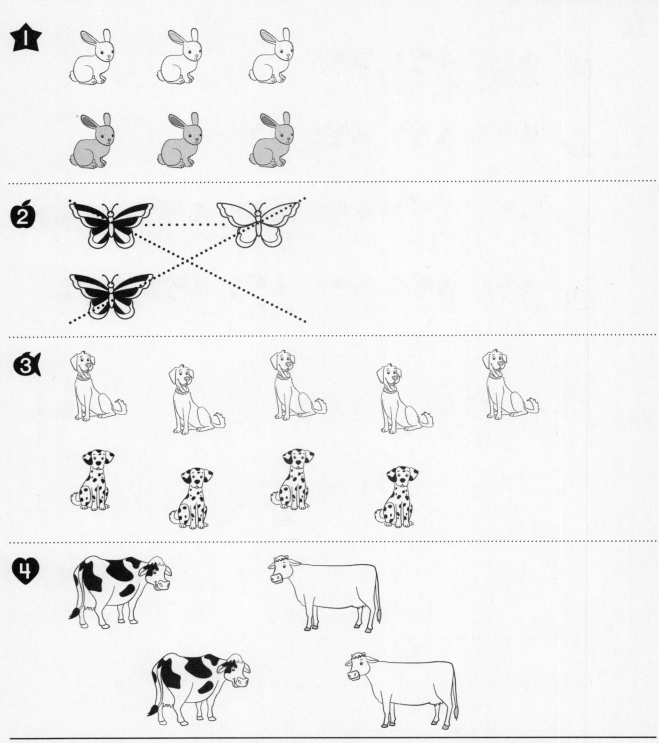

Directions Say: ⭐ *Look at the rabbits in each row. Draw a line from each white rabbit to a gray rabbit. There are the same number, or an* **equal** *number, of rabbits in each group. How do you know the groups are equal?* 🍎 *Draw lines to match the butterflies from one group to the other. The two groups are NOT equal. How do you know the groups are NOT equal? Mark an X on the two groups;* ✈️ *and* ❤️ *Draw lines from the animals in one group to the animals in the other group. Draw a circle around the groups if they are equal in number, or mark an X on the groups if they are NOT equal in number.* **On the Back!** Have students draw a group of 4 objects. Then have them draw a group of objects that is equal in number to the first group.

1

Ⓐ

Ⓑ

Ⓒ

Ⓓ

2

3

5

4

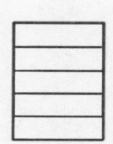 **2**

Directions Have students: ⭐ mark the picture that shows three; 🍎 count the windows on the house, and then color the boxes to show how many.

Name _____

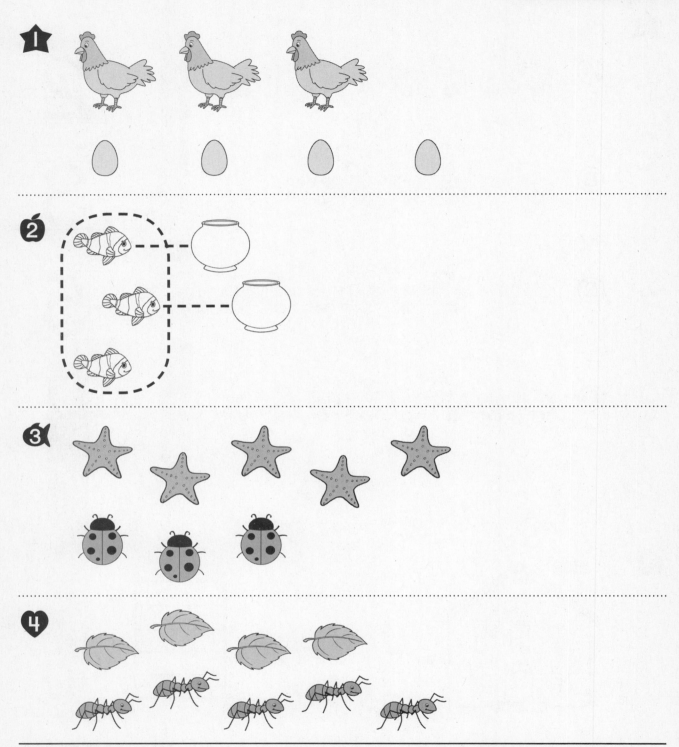

Directions ❶ Say: *Look at the row of hens and eggs. Draw lines to match each hen to an egg, and then draw a circle around the group that has more. There are more eggs than hens. So, the number of eggs is* **greater than** *the number of hens.* Have students draw lines to match objects from one group to the other. Say: ❷ *Which group has more, the group of fish or the group of fishbowls? How do you know? Draw a circle around the group that is greater in number;* ❸ *and* ❹ *Draw a circle around the group that is greater in number. Explain how you know you are correct.* **On the Back!** Have students draw a group of counters. Then have them draw a group of counters that is greater in number than the first group, and explain why their picture is correct.

Play a Game

Partner Talk
Share your thinking while you work.

Start Get 20 red squares.

Put [1] [2] [3] [4] [5] in a ⛰.

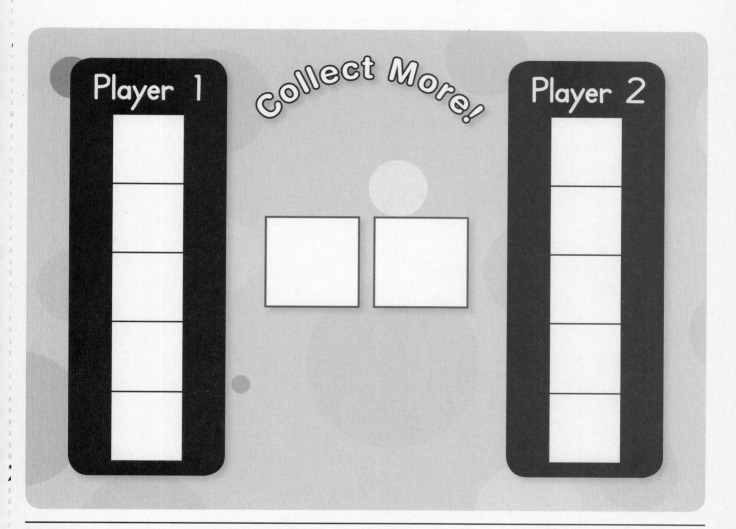

Player 1   Collect More!   Player 2

Materials	Number tiles 1–5, a bag for the tiles, 20 red squares
Oral Directions	**TRY** Give 10 red squares to one player. Give 10 red squares to the other player. Choose a game board. Each player picks a number tile from the bag. Put your tile in the tile space next to your game board. Put that many red squares on your game board. The player who has the greater number of squares on a game board keeps all the red squares. Remove the tiles and each player takes another turn. The player who collects the most red squares wins.

TRY AGAIN If you have time, play again! |

Play a Game

Start  Get 10 red squares.

Put ⊡ ② ③ ④ ⑤ in a 🛍.

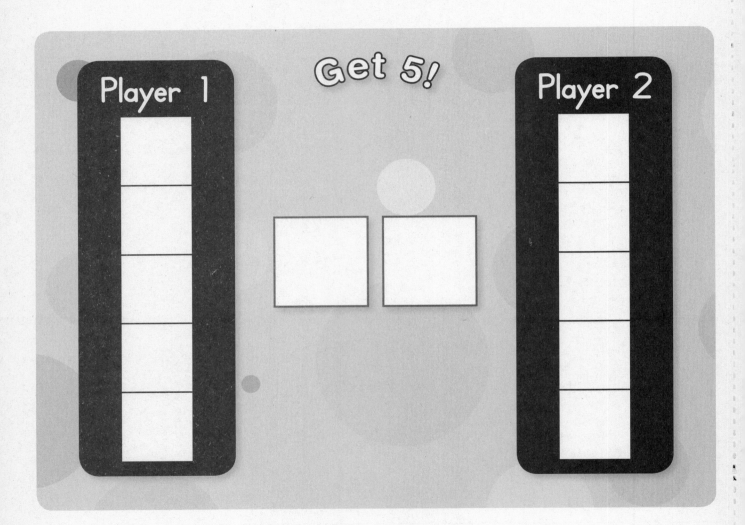

Player 1

Get 5!

Player 2

Materials	Number tiles 1–5, a bag for the tiles, 10 red squares
Oral Directions	**TRY** Give 1 game board to each player. Each player picks a tile from the bag. Put your tile in the tile space next to your game board. If you have the greater number, explain why. Put a square on your game board. Put the tiles back in the bag and play again. The first player to get 5 squares wins. **TRY AGAIN** If you have time, play again!

Name _____

 1

(A) 2

(B) 3

(C) 4

(D) 5

2

Directions Have students: **1** mark the number that tells how many apples; **2** draw lines to match the sandwiches in one group to the other. Then have them draw a circle around the groups if they are equal in number, or mark an X on the groups if they are NOT equal in number.

D 2·3

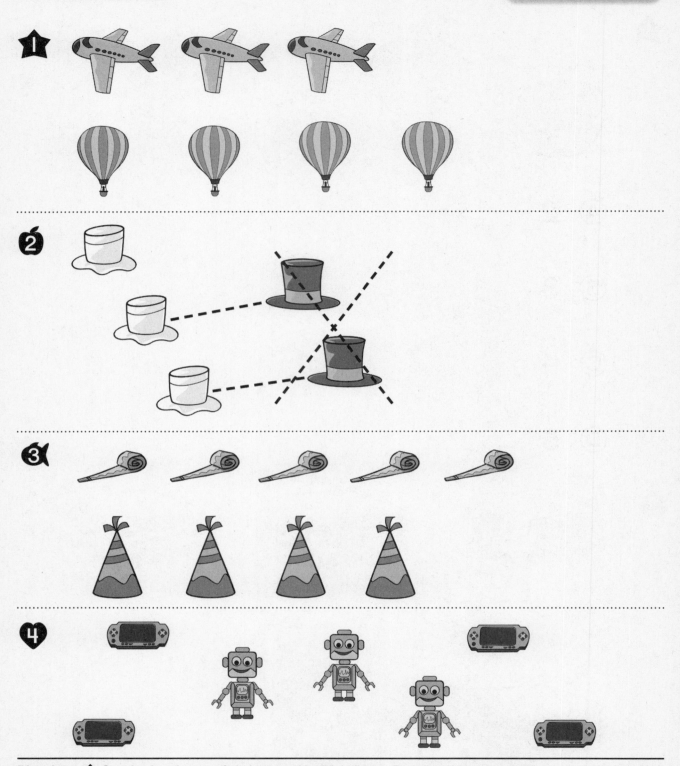

Directions ⭐ Say: *Look at the row of airplanes and hot air balloons. Draw lines between rows to match each airplane to a hot air balloon. The number of airplanes is* **less than** *the number of hot air balloons. Mark an X on the group that is less in number than the other group.* Have students draw lines to match objects from one group to the other. Say: ❷ *Which group of hats is less in number? Mark an X on that group;* ❸ and ❹ *Mark an X on the group that is less in number than the other group, and then explain why you are correct.* **On the Back!** Have students draw two different groups of objects. Then have them mark an X on the group that is less in number, and then explain why they are correct.

Name _____

 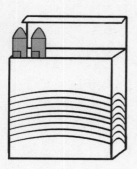

Ⓐ 2

Ⓑ 3

Ⓒ 4

Ⓓ 5

Directions Have students: ⭐ mark the number that tells how many crayons are in the box; ② draw a circle around the group of cats that is equal in number to the first group of cats.

Name _____

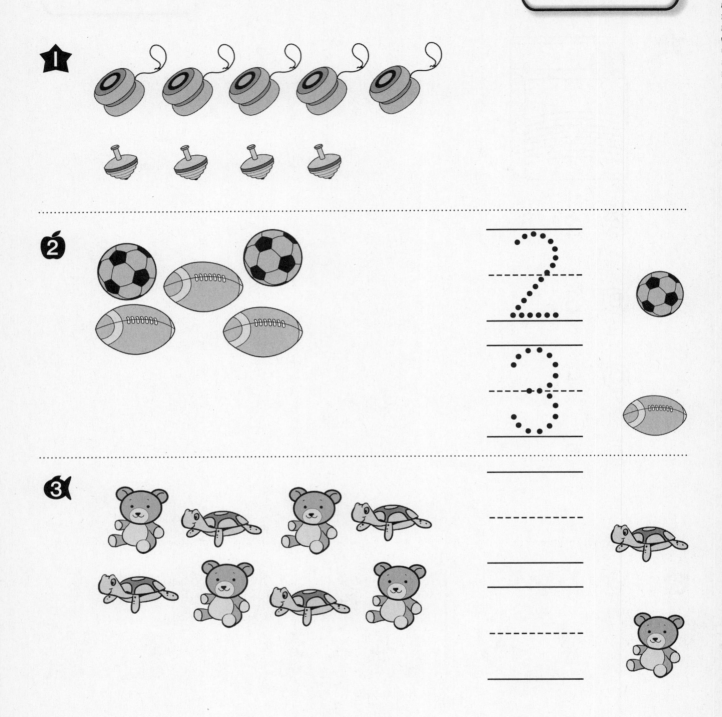

Directions Say: ⭐ *Look at the **group** of yo-yos and tops. Let's compare the number of toys in each group. How many yo-yos are there? How many tops are there? Draw a circle around the group of toys that is greater in number than the other group of toys;* ② *How many soccer balls are there? How many footballs are there? Write the numbers to tell how many. Draw a circle around the number that is greater than the other number. Mark an X on the number that is less than the other number.* ③ *Have students count the toys, write the numbers to tell how many, and then draw a circle around the number that is greater than the other number and mark an X on the number that is less than the other number, or draw a circle around both numbers if they are equal.* **On the Back!** *Have students draw 3 toys. Then have them draw a group of toys less than the first group, and then write the numbers to tell how many.*

Name _____

(A)

(B)

(C)

(D)

❷

Directions Have students: ❶ mark the picture that shows 3 cups; ❷ draw lines to match objects from one group to the other. Have them draw a circle around the group that is greater in number than the other group, and then explain why they are correct.

Name _____

★ 5

3

② X

3

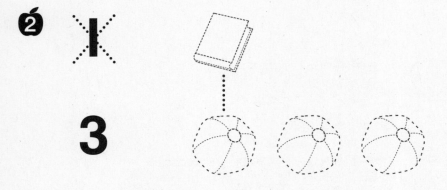

③ 4

4

④ 2

0

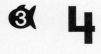

Directions Say: **★** *Pictures can help you* **compare** *numbers. Draw lines to match each sand dollar to a shell. Which group is greater in number? Draw a circle around the number of that group.* **②** *Draw 1 book. Now draw 3 beach balls. Use the pictures to help you compare the numbers. Mark an X on the number that is less than the other number;* **③** *and* **④** *Compare the numbers. Draw a circle around the number that is greater than the other number, or draw a circle around both numbers if they are equal.* Have students draw pictures to show how they know. **On the Back!** Have students write two different numbers, and then mark an X on the number that is less than the other number. Have them draw pictures to show how they know.

R 2•5

Ⓐ 5

Ⓑ 4

Ⓒ 3

Ⓓ 2

Directions Have students: ★ mark the number that tells how many frogs; ❷ count the birds, and then write the numbers to tell how many. Then have them draw a circle around the number that is greater than the other number and mark an X on the number that is less than the other number.

Name _____

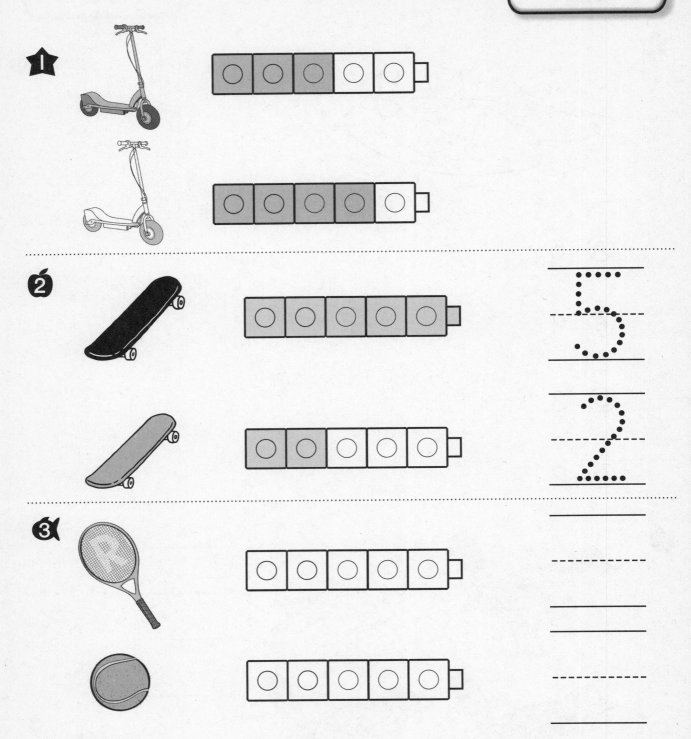

Directions Say: ⭐ *You can use cubes to* **model** *which group of scooters is greater in number than the other group. Look at the 2 cube trains. The colored cubes show how many of each color scooter. Compare the number of colored cubes, and then draw a circle around the cube train that has a greater number of colored cubes;* ❷ *Marco has 5 black skateboards and 2 gray skateboards. Color the first cube train to show how many black skateboards. Color the second cube train to show how many gray skateboards. Write the numbers that tell how many, and then mark an X on the number that is less than the other number;* ❸ *Emily has 2 tennis rackets and 4 tennis balls. Color the cubes to show how many, write the numbers that tell how many, and then draw a circle around the greater number.* **On the Back!** *Have students draw two different groups of objects, and then tell a story involving greater than or less than.*

R 2·6

Play a Game

Partner
Talk

Share your thinking while you work.

Start  Get 5 red squares.
Get 5 blue squares.
Get a 🎲 .

Sock Chart

Toss	Cover this number of socks on the game board.
⚀	🧦
⚁	🧦🧦
⚂	🧦🧦🧦
⚃	🧦🧦🧦🧦
⚄	🧦🧦🧦🧦🧦

Win With Five

Materials   5 red squares, 5 blue squares, 1 number cube

Oral Directions   **TRY** Give 5 red squares to one player. Give 5 blue squares to the other player. Take turns. Toss the number cube. If you see 6 dots, toss again. Look at the *Sock Chart*. Find your number of dots in the chart. Count the socks next to those dots. Look at the *Win With Five* game board. If you see the same number of socks, cover them with a square. If you do NOT see the same number of socks, your turn is over. Take turns until one player gets 5 squares on the game board.

TRY AGAIN If you have time, play again! This time, tell your partner how you know the number of socks on the game board is the same as the number of socks in the chart.

Play a Game

 Get 5 red squares.
Get 5 blue squares.
Get a 🎲 .

Sock Chart

Toss	Cover a group of socks that is greater in number than this number of socks.
⚀	🧦
⚁	🧦 🧦
⚂	🧦 🧦 🧦
⚃	🧦 🧦 🧦 🧦
⚄	🧦 🧦 🧦 🧦 🧦

Win With Five

🧦🧦🧦 🧦🧦	🧦	🧦🧦 🧦
🧦🧦 🧦🧦	🧦🧦🧦	🧦🧦
🧦 🧦	🧦🧦 🧦🧦	🧦🧦🧦 🧦🧦🧦

Materials   5 red squares, 5 blue squares, 1 number cube

Oral Directions   **TRY** Give 5 red squares to one player. Give 5 blue squares to the other player. Take turns. Toss the number cube. If you see 6 dots, toss again. Look at the *Sock Chart*. Find your number of dots in the chart. Count the socks next to those dots. Look at the *Win With Five* game board. Point to a picture on the game board that is greater in number than the ones you counted in the chart. Cover that picture with a square. If you do not find a picture to cover on the game board, your turn is over. Take turns until one player gets 5 squares on the game board.

TRY AGAIN If you have time, play again! This time, point to a picture that is equal in number or less in number than the ones you counted in the chart.

This book belongs to: _____

Fun in the Sun

Illustrated by Jenny B Harris

Written by Suzanne Belahnira

We can have fun
at the sea!

We can count ___ sun

and ___ umbrellas.

fold down

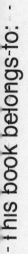

We can count ___ balls.

We can count ___

___ crabs. We all can

have fun at the sea!

We can count ____ hats.

We can count ____ mats

and ____ bags.

fold up

We can count ____ trees.

We can count ____ fish

and ____ starfish.

Name _____

Numbers 6 to 10

Topic 3 Standards
K.CC.A.3, K.CC.B.4a, K.CC.B.4b, K.CC.B.5, K.OA.A.3
See the front of the Student's Edition for complete standards.

Dear Family,

Your child is learning about numbers from 6 to 10. He or she will learn how to represent these quantities with objects and how to read and write them as numbers. This topic will also show your child how to make 10 by combining two other quantities.

Ways to Show a Number
The last number said tells the number of objects in a group regardless of their arrangement or order.

There are different ways to show the number 8.

Try this activity with your child to practice showing and writing numbers 6 to 10.

Draw Pictures

Say a number from 6 to 10. Ask your child to show that number by drawing the appropriate number of simple objects (balls, flowers, smiley faces, stars), and then writing the number. Continue with the other numbers. When completed, have your child hold up, or point to, the picture that shows 6 objects; 7 objects; 8 objects; and so on.

Observe Your Child

Focus on Mathematical Practice 6:
Attend to precision.

Help your child become proficient with Mathematical Practice 6. When your child writes a number, make sure he or she is writing the correct symbol. If your child has trouble writing the number, write it out first, and then have him or her trace the number you wrote.

Nombre _____

Números del 6 al 10

Estándares del Tema 3
K.CNC.A.3, K.CNC.B.4a, K.CNC.B.4b, K.CNC.B.5, K.OA.A.3
Los estándares completos se encuentran en las páginas preliminares del
Libro del estudiante.

Estimada familia:

Su niño(a) está aprendiendo sobre los números del 6 al 10. Aprenderá cómo representar estas cantidades con objetos y cómo leerlas y escribirlas como números. Este tema también le mostrará a su niño(a) cómo formar 10 al combinar otras dos cantidades.

Maneras de mostrar un número
El último número que se dice indica el número de objetos que hay en un grupo, sin importar su ordenación u orden.

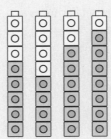

Hay diferentes maneras de mostrar el número 8.

Intente realizar esta actividad con su niño(a) para practicar cómo mostrar y escribir los números del 6 al 10.

Hacer dibujos

Diga un número del 6 al 10. Pida a su niño(a) que muestre ese número dibujando el número apropiado de objetos (pelotas, flores, caritas sonrientes, estrellas) y luego escriba el número. Continúe con los demás números. Cuando termine, pida a sus niño(a) que sostenga, o señale, el dibujo que muestra 6 objetos; 7 objetos; 8 objetos; y así sucesivamente.

Observe a su niño(a)

Enfoque en la Práctica matemática 6:
Prestar atención a la precisión.

Ayude a su niño(a) a adquirir competencia en la Práctica matemática 6. Cuando su niño(a) escriba un número, asegúrese de que escriba el símbolo correcto. Si tiene dificultad para escribir el número, escríbalo usted primero y luego pida a su niño(a) que trace el número que usted escribió.

Frogs

 ①

_____

- -

_____

· ·

 ②

_____

- -

_____

· ·

③

_____

- -

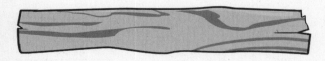

_____

Directions Say: *Most frogs are cold-blooded creatures and live in warm weather areas. There are some frogs, like the wood frog, that have adapted to survive in freezing weather.* Have students draw: ① 6 frogs (or counters) on the log, and then practice writing the number that tells how many; ② 7 frogs (or counters) on the log, and then practice writing the number that tells how many; ③ 8 frogs (or counters) on the log, and then practice writing the number that tells how many.
Extension Have students draw a picture that shows 9 animals that live in cold weather areas, and then practice writing the number that tells how many.

Name _____

Leopards

_____

– – – – – – – – –

_____

_____

– – – – – – – – –

_____

_____

– – – – – – – – –

_____

Directions Say: *Did you know leopards can be different colors depending on where they live? Leopards in grasslands are yellow. Leopards that live in snowy areas are gray.* Have students: ❶ and ❷ count the leopards, and then write the numbers that tell how many; ❸ draw 10 spots on the leopard, and then write the number that tells how many.
Extension Have students describe the weather in the rainforest. Have them draw up to 10 animals that live in the rainforest, and then write the number that tells how many.

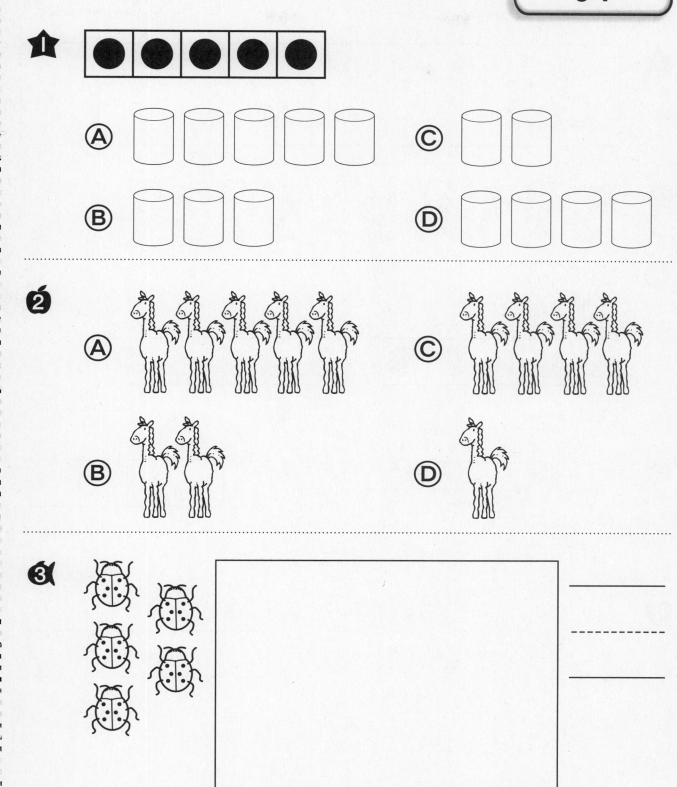

Directions Have students: ⭐ mark the picture that shows the same number of blocks as counters; 🍎 mark the picture that shows 5 horses; 🐟 draw a group of bugs that is less in number than the group shown, and then write the number that tells how many.

1

2

3

4

Directions Say: **1** *Look at the groups of chickens. Let's count them. Draw a circle around the group with* **six** *chickens. Color the group with* **seven** *chickens;* **2** *How many cows are there? Draw a circle around the counters that show how many;* **3** *How many sheep are there? Draw counters to show how many;* **4** *How many ducks are there? Draw counters to show how many.* **On the Back!** *Have students draw 6 or 7 counters, and then tell how many they drew.*

Play a Game

Start 👫 Get 12 red squares.

Memory Match

Materials   12 red squares

Oral Directions   **TRY** Cover every game space with a square. Take turns. Uncover two game spaces. Count the objects in each space aloud. If the number of objects in each game space is the same, keep the squares. If not, put the squares back where they were. Keep playing until every game space is uncovered. The player who collects more squares wins.

TRY AGAIN If you have time, play again!

 # Play a Game

 **Start** 👥 Get 12 red squares.

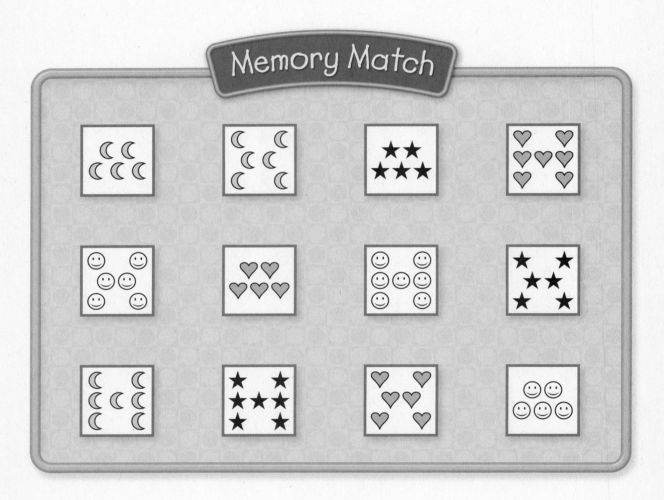
Memory Match

Materials   12 red squares

Oral Directions   **TRY** Cover every game space with a square. Take turns. Uncover two game spaces. Count the objects in each space aloud. If the number of objects in each game space is different, keep the squares. If the number of objects in each game space is the same, put the squares back where they were. Keep playing until you cannot uncover any more game spaces. The player who collects more squares wins.

TRY AGAIN If you have time, play again!

0   I   2   3

Ⓐ   Ⓑ   Ⓒ   Ⓓ

2

Ⓐ

Ⓑ

Ⓒ

Ⓓ

3

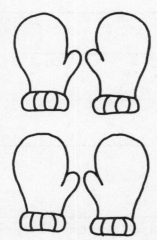

Directions Have students: ⭐ mark the number that tells how many books; 🍎 mark the picture that shows 6 counters; ⭐ draw a group of mittens that is less in number than the group shown.

D 3·2

Name _____

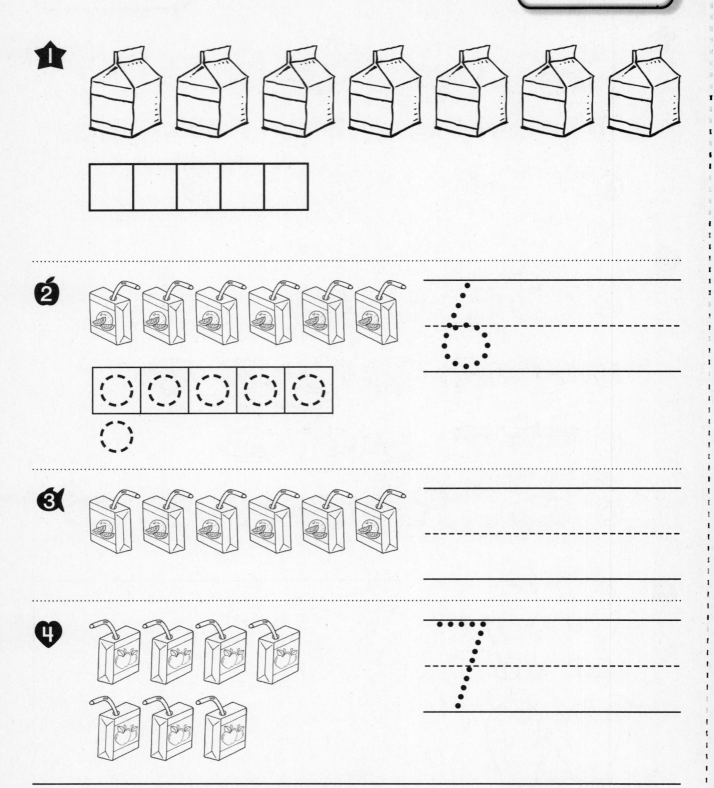

Directions Say: ⭐ *Look at the milk cartons. Let's* **count** *them together: 1, 2, 3, 4, 5, 6, 7. Draw counters to show how many milk cartons;* ❷ *How many juice boxes are there? Draw counters to show how many, and then practice writing the number that tells how many;* ❸ *and* ❹ *How many juice boxes are there? Practice writing the numbers that tell how many.* **On the Back!** *Have students draw groups of 6 and 7 objects, and then practice writing the numbers that tell how many.*

⭐ **1**

Ⓐ

Ⓑ

Ⓒ

Ⓓ

🍎 **2**

Ⓐ

Ⓑ

Ⓒ

Ⓓ

🐟 **3**

Directions Have students: ⭐ mark the picture that shows 7 geese; 🍎 mark the picture that shows 4 counters; 🐟 count the number of water bottles, and then practice writing the number that tells how many.

D 3·3

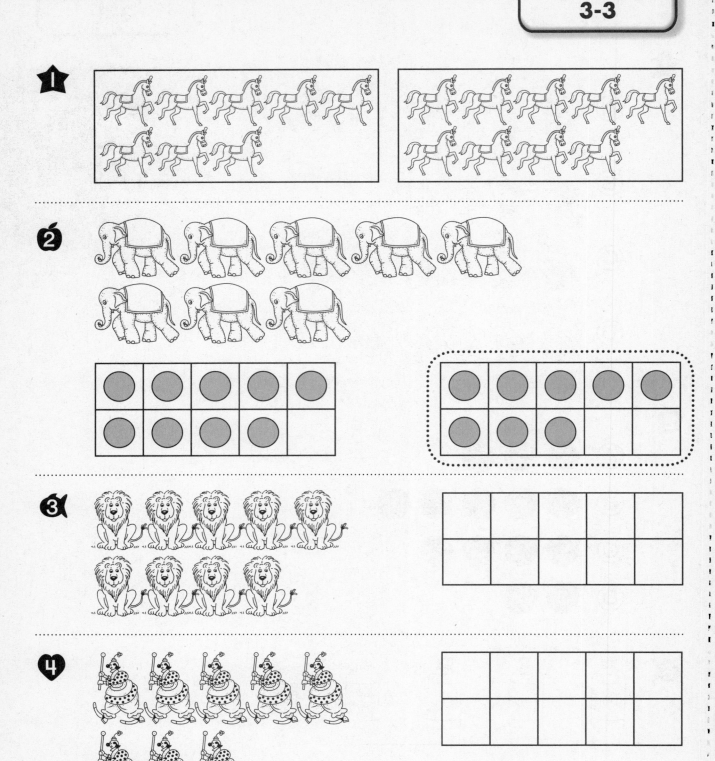

1

2

3

4

Directions Say: **1** *Look at the groups of horses. Let's count them. Draw a circle around the group with **eight** horses. Color the group with **nine** horses;* **2** *How many elephants are there? Draw a circle around the counters that show how many;* **3** *How many lions are there? Draw counters to show how many;* **4** *How many clowns are there? Draw counters to show how many.* **On the Back!** *Have students draw 8 or 9 counters, and then tell how many they drew.*

Helping Hands

Start 👤 or 👥 Put  0 1 2 3 4 5 6 7 8 9 in a 🛍.

Materials	Number tiles 0 – 9, a bag for the tiles
Oral Directions	**TRY** If you have a partner, take turns. Pick 3 tiles. Line them up on the line on the left. Pick 4 tiles. Line them up on the line on the right. Start at the left. Read the numbers. Press the keys to dial the numbers. Put the tiles back in the bag.
	TRY AGAIN If you have time, play again! This time, pick new tiles and dial a different number.

Helping Hands

Start 👤 or 👥 Get 📝.

555-9978

555-9876

555-7829

555-8349

Materials   Paper and a pencil

Oral Directions

TRY If you have a partner, take turns. Pick a telephone number on this page. Write that telephone number on your paper. Press the keys to dial the number. Do this for every number.

TRY AGAIN If you have time, make up a telephone number. Say and dial that number.

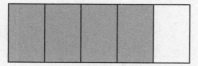

Ⓐ 0

Ⓑ 1

Ⓒ 2

Ⓓ 3

Directions Have students: ⭐ mark the picture that shows 5 shaded boxes; 🍎 mark the number that tells how many babies are in the baby buggy; 🐟 draw 9 counters in the ten-frame.

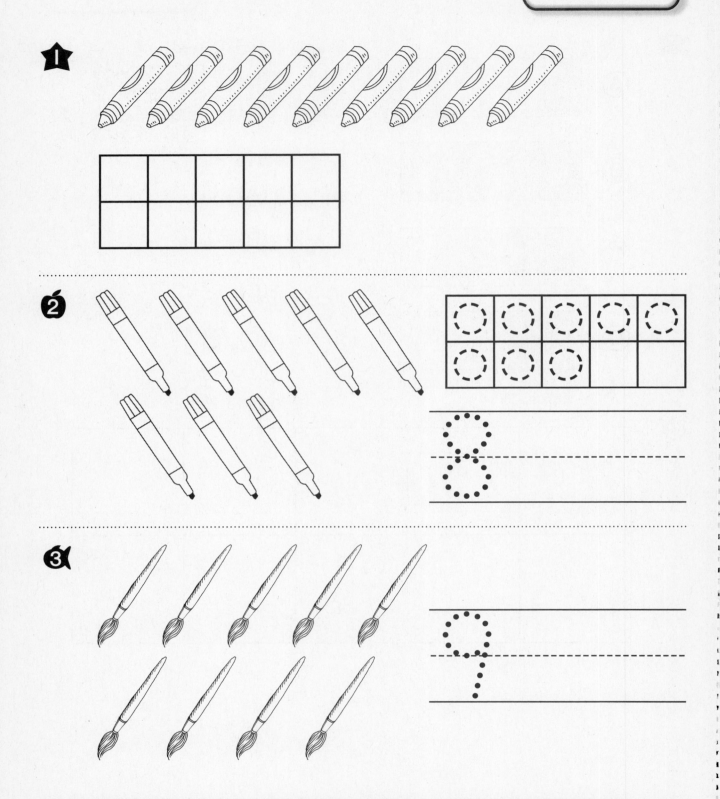

Directions Say: ⭐ *Look at the crayons. Let's count them together. There are* **nine** *crayons. Draw counters to show how many crayons;* 🍎 *How many markers are there? Draw counters to show how many, and then practice writing the number that tells how many;* 🔷 *How many paintbrushes are there? Practice writing the number that tells how many.*
On the Back! Have students draw groups of 8 and 9 objects, and then practice writing the numbers that tell how many.

1

2

3

4

5

Ⓐ Ⓒ

Ⓑ  Ⓓ

2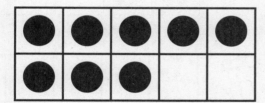

6   7   8   9

Ⓐ   Ⓑ   Ⓒ   Ⓓ

---

3 **3**

  |

Directions Have students: **1** mark the picture that shows the missing number of cubes when counting in order from 1 to 5; **2** mark the number that tells how many counters; **3** compare the numbers. Then have them mark an X on the number that is less than the other number, or both numbers if they are equal. Have students draw pictures to show how they know.

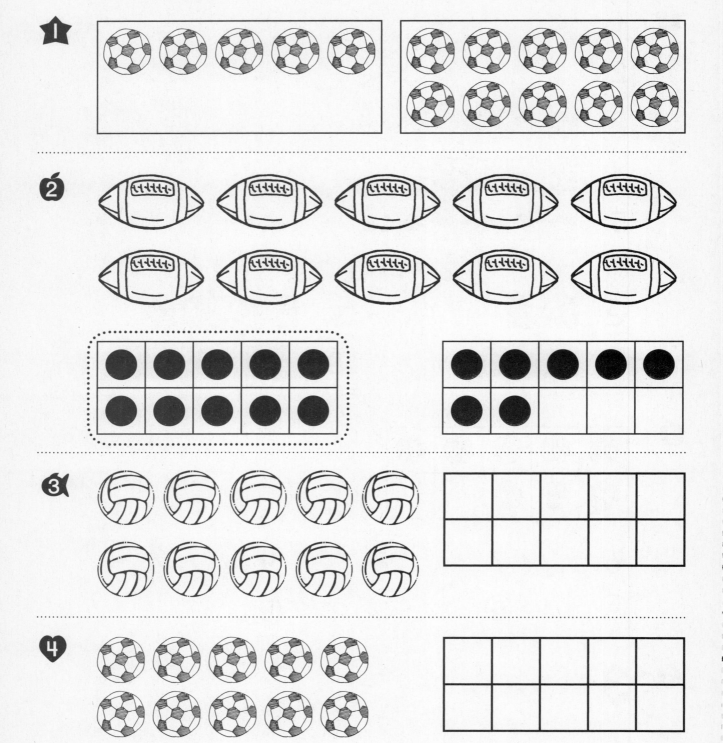

Directions Say: ⭐ Look at the groups of soccer balls. Let's count them. Draw a circle around the group with **ten** soccer balls; ② How many footballs are there? Draw a circle around the counters that show how many; ③ How many volleyballs are there? Draw counters to show how many; ④ How many soccer balls are there? Draw counters to show how many.
On the Back! Have students draw 10 counters, and then tell how many they drew.

Play a Game

Start  Get 20 squares. Get a .

FRONT BACK

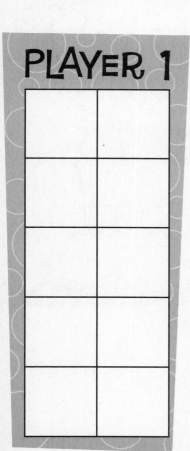

PLAYER 1

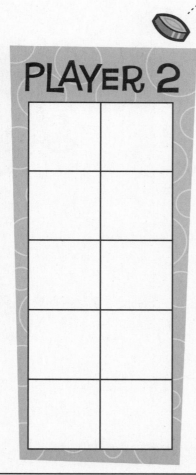

PLAYER 2

Materials   20 squares, 1 penny

Oral Directions   **TRY** Look at the front and the back of the coin. Talk about what is on the front. Talk about what is on the back. Practice tossing the coin. Tell which side you see. Then take turns to play a game. Choose a game board. Put 10 squares on it. On your turn, make a guess. Say "front" or "back" before you toss the coin. Toss the coin. Look at the coin to see if it is the same as your guess. If it is, take a square off your game board. If the coin is NOT the same as your guess, your turn is over. Take turns until one player collects 10 squares.

TRY AGAIN If you have time, play again!

Play a Game

Partner Talk
Share your thinking while you work.

Start 👥 Get 20 squares. Get a and a .

 FRONT

 BACK

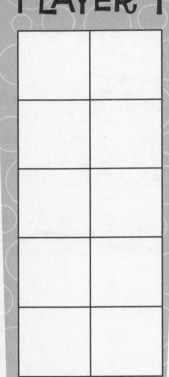

PLAYER 1

PLAYER 2

Materials 20 squares, 2 pennies

Oral Directions **TRY** Look at the front and the back of the coin. Talk about what is on the front. Talk about what is on the back. Toss the coins a few times. Tell if you see two fronts, two backs, or one front and one back. Then take turns to play a game. Choose a game board. Fill it with 10 squares. Take turns. Toss both coins. If you see two fronts, the player with that game board removes a square. If you see two backs, the player with that game board removes a square. If you see a front and a back, no one removes a square. The first player to collect 10 squares wins.

TRY AGAIN If you have time, play again! This time, play on the other game board.

Name _____

 1

Ⓐ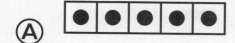

Ⓒ

Ⓑ

Ⓓ

2

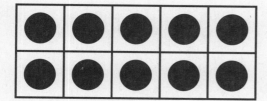

10   9   1   0

Ⓐ   Ⓑ   Ⓒ   Ⓓ

3

_____

- - - - - - - - - - - - - - - - - - -

_____

Directions Have students: **1** mark the picture that shows 7 counters; **2** mark the number that tells how many counters; **3** count the dolphins, and then practice writing the number that tells how many.

D 3·6

Name _____

 1

2

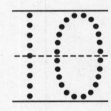

3

_____

- - - - - - - - - -

_____

Directions Say: 1 *Look at the **group** of walruses and group of seals. Let's count how many in each group. Draw a circle around the group of animals that shows 10;* 2 *How many polar bears are there? Write the number that tells how many;* 3 *How many penguins are there? Write the number that tells how many.* **On the Back!** Have students draw a group of 10 objects, and then write the number that tells how many.

R 3•6

Name _____

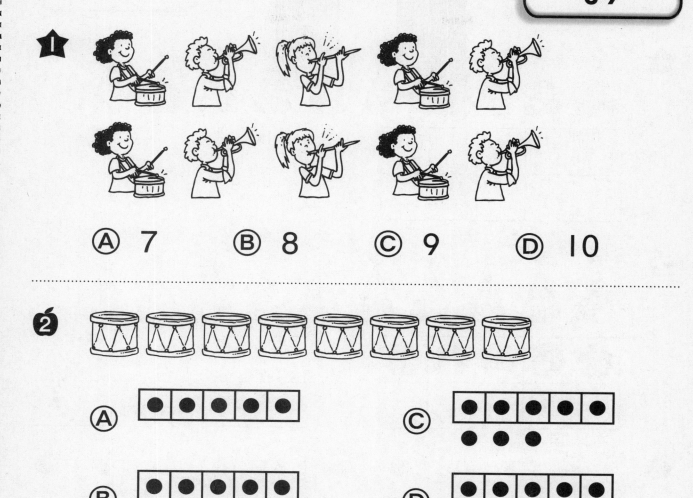

1

Ⓐ 7   Ⓑ 8   Ⓒ 9   Ⓓ 10

2

3

Directions Have students: **1** mark the number that tells how many children; **2** mark the picture that shows how many drums; **3** count the pineapples, and then color the boxes to show how many.

Name _____

1

2

5 and 5

3

_____ and _____

4

_____ and _____

Directions Say: **1** *Look at the party hats. Let's **count** them. Draw 10 counters to show how many;* **2** *How many black counters are there? How many white counters are there? This shows one way to make 10. Color 5 party hats red and 5 yellow to show that way. Now write the numbers 5 and 5 to show the parts;* **3** *Count the black and white counters, color the party horns red and yellow to show this way to show 10, and then write the numbers;* **4** *Draw red and yellow counters to show another way to make 10, color the smiley faces red and yellow to show that way, and then write the numbers.* **On the Back!** *Have students draw red and yellow counters to show a different way to make 10, and then write the numbers.*

Name _____

⭐**1**

4	8	9	10
Ⓐ	Ⓑ	Ⓒ	Ⓓ

🍎**2**

_____

- - - - - - - - - -

_____

Directions Have students: ⭐ mark the number that tells how many cats; 🍎 draw 10 counters or objects, and then write the number that tells how many.

Name _____

★1

②

③

④

✋5

Directions Say: **★1** *Here are some frogs. Let's count how many: 1, 2, 3, 4. How many frogs are colored? Write the* **number** *0 to tell how many are colored. How many frogs are white? Write the number 4 to tell how many are white. This shows one way to make 4. We can show all the different ways to make 4;* **②** *Trace the number on the left. Color that number of frogs. How many white frogs are there? Write the number to tell how many.* **③** – **✋5** *Have students use two different color crayons to complete the pattern showing ways to make 4, and then write the numbers. Have them explain the pattern.* **On the Back!** *Have students show all the ways to make 3 using counters.*

Math in Motion

Start 👫 Put 4 5 in a 🛍️.

4   5

Materials	Number tiles 4 and 5, a bag for the tiles
Oral Directions	**TRY** Tap your left foot on the floor four times. Tap your right foot on the floor four times. Tap your left foot on the floor five times. Tap your right foot on the floor five times. Take turns. Pick a tile. If you pick 4, choose a way to make 4 by tapping part of 4 with one foot and part of 4 with the other foot. Point to the way you chose on the activity page. Tap your way to make 4. Ask your partner to tap your way to make 4. If you pick 5, choose a way to make 5 by tapping part of 5 with one foot and part of 5 with the other foot. Point to the way you chose on the activity page. Tap your way to make 5. Ask your partner to tap your way to make 5. Put the tile back in the bag. Repeat until each partner picks a tile four times.

TRY AGAIN If you have time, begin again! This time, after you tap your number, ask your partner to tap the same number in a different way.

Math in Motion

Start 👫 Put 4 5 in a 🛍.

4

5

Materials	Number tiles 4 and 5, a bag for the tiles
Oral Directions	**TRY** Tap your feet on the floor. Show all the ways to make 4. Show all the ways to make 5. Then let your partner show all the ways to make 4, and all the ways to make 5. Then take turns. On your turn, pick a tile. Point to a way to tap that number on the activity page. Tap your feet that way. Ask your partner to make that number by tapping in a different way. Put the tile back in the bag. Repeat until each partner picks a tile four times.
	TRY AGAIN If you have time, begin again! This time, make up a dance to help your class remember the parts of 4 or the parts of 5.

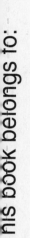
This book belongs to:

Jake's Garden

Written by Paige Lemisky
Illustrated by Sheree Boyd

Plant with me.

Let's make rows.

1, 2, 3, 4, ___ rows.

Topic 4 · 1

fold down

You planted with me.

Now we have

___ rows.

A garden for me!

Topic 4 · 4

Plant with me.

Let's make 1 more.

Now we have

_____ rows.

fold up

Plant with me.

Let's make more rows.

Now we have

_____ rows.

Name _____

Compare Numbers 0 to 10

Topic 4 Standards
K.CC.A.2, K.CC.B.4c, K.CC.C.6, K.CC.C.7
See the front of the Student's Edition for complete standards.

Dear Family,

Your child is learning to compare numbers from 0 to 10. In this topic, he or she will learn to compare numbers using groups of objects to determine which number is greater. He or she will also learn to compare groups of numbers by counting.

Comparing Groups
Count the objects in a group, write the number to tell how many in each group, and then compare groups of objects as greater or less than a specific number.

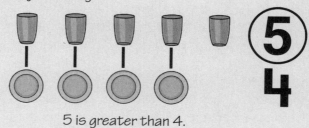

5 is greater than 4.

Here is an activity to do with your child to practice comparing numbers 0 to 10.

Compare the Stars

Draw 6 stars on a sheet of paper and ask your child to count them. Have him or her draw a group of stars that is less in number than the number of stars they counted, and then write the number. Now ask your child to draw 6 to 9 stars and write the number to tell how many. Say, "I will draw a group of stars greater in number than the group you drew." Have him or her count the stars, write the number that tells how many, and then circle the number that is greater than the other. Repeat the activity using different numbers.

Observe Your Child

Focus on Mathematical Practice 2:
Reason abstractly and quantitatively.

Help your child become proficient with Mathematical Practice 2. Draw a group of 4 stars and a group of 7 stars. Have your child write the numbers that tell how many in each group. Then have them tell which number is greater than the other, and explain how they know.

Nombre _____

Comparar los números del 0 al 10

Estándares del Tema 4

K.CNC.A.2, K.CNC.B.4c, K.CNC.C.6, K.CNC.C.7
Los estándares completos se encuentran en las páginas preliminares del
Libro del estudiante.

Estimada familia:

Su niño(a) está aprendiendo a comparar los números del 0 al 10. En este tema, aprenderá a comparar los números usando grupos de objetos para determinar qué número es mayor. También aprenderá a comparar grupos de números mediante el conteo.

Comparar grupos

Cuenta los objetos en un grupo, escribe el número para indicar cuántos hay en cada grupo y luego compara grupos de objetos para saber si son mayor o menor que un número específico.

5 es mayor que 4.

Esta es una actividad que puede hacer con su niño(a) para practicar la comparación de los números del 0 al 10.

Comparar las estrellas

Dibuje 6 estrellas en una hoja de papel y pida a su niño(a) que las cuente. Pida a su niño(a) que dibuje un grupo de estrellas que tenga un número menor que el número de estrellas que contó y luego escriba el número. Ahora pídale que dibuje de 6 a 9 estrellas y escriba el número para indicar cuántas hay. Diga: "Voy a dibujar un grupo de estrellas con un número mayor que el grupo que dibujaste". Pida a su niño(a) que cuente las estrellas, escriba el número que indica cuántas hay y luego encierre en un círculo el número que es mayor que el otro. Repita la actividad usando diferentes números.

Observe a su niño(a)

Enfoque en la Práctica matemática 2:

Razonar de manera abstracta y cuantitativa.

Ayude a su niño(a) a adquirir competencia en la Práctica matemática 2. Dibuje un grupo de 2 estrellas y un grupo de 7 estrellas. Pida a su niño(a) que escriba los números que indican cuántos hay en cada grupo. Luego pídale que indique qué número es mayor y que explique cómo lo sabe.

Name _____

Clouds

Directions Say: *Did you know that clouds are made of water droplets or ice crystals? Not all clouds produce rain or snow.* Have students count the number of gray and white clouds, write the number to tell how many, and then: ⭐ draw a circle around both numbers if they are equal, or mark an X on both numbers if they are NOT equal; 🍎 draw a circle around the number that is greater than the other number; 🕊 mark an X on the number that is less than the other number.
Extension Have students draw 2 clouds. Then have them draw a group of clouds that is greater in number, and a different group of clouds that is less in number than the first group they drew. Write the numbers to tell how many in each group.

Name _____

Rain and Snow

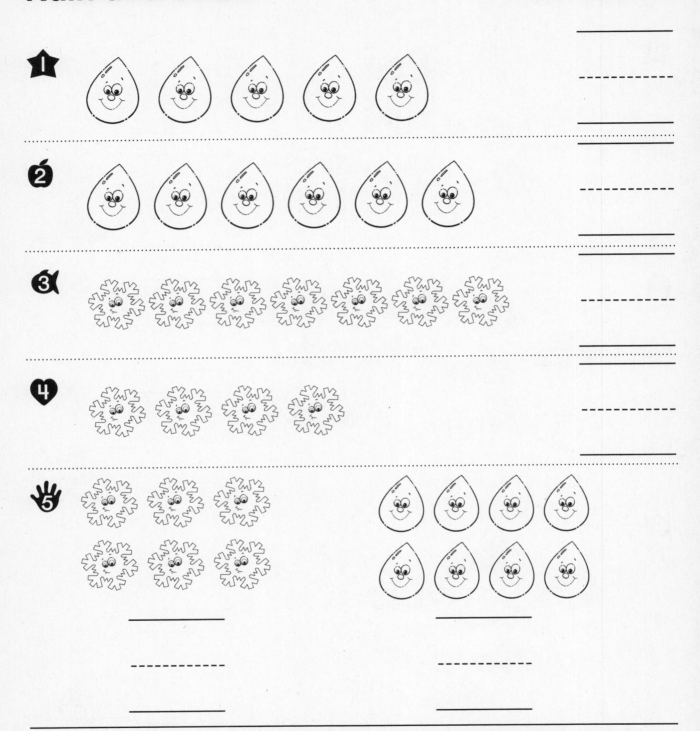

Directions Say: *Did you know that rain and snow are both made from water? Snow happens more in cold weather and rain happens more in warmer weather.* Have students use reasoning to find the number that is: ⭐–❸ 1 greater than the raindrops or snowflakes shown. Draw counters to show the answer, and then write the number. Have students explain their reasoning; ❹ 2 greater than the snowflakes shown. Draw counters to show the answer, and then write the number. Have students explain their reasoning. ✋ Have students count the snowflakes and raindrops, write the numbers to tell how many in each group, and then draw a circle around the number that is greater than the other number.
Extension Have students draw a picture that shows 4 objects, and then have them draw a group with 1 more and another group with 2 more than the first group they drew. Write the numbers to tell how many in each group.

1

Ⓐ

Ⓒ

Ⓑ

Ⓓ

 2

Ⓐ

Ⓒ

Ⓑ

Ⓓ

 3

_____

- - - - - - - - - - - - - - - - - - - -

_____

Directions Have students: **1** mark the picture that shows the fishbowl with 0 fish; **2** mark the picture that shows 2 birds on a branch; **3** count the stars, and then practice writing the number that tells how many.

D 4·1

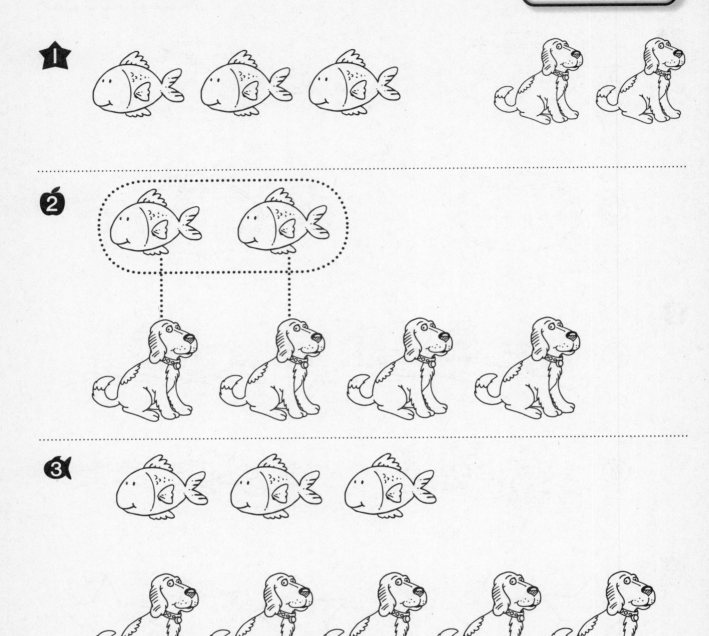

Directions Say: ⭐ *We use the words* greater than *and* less than *to* **compare** *groups of objects. Look at the two groups of pets. Draw a circle around the group that is greater than the other group. How do you know you are correct?* ❷ *Look at the group of pets. Draw a line from each fish in the top row to a dog in the bottom row, and then draw a circle around the group that is less than the other group;* ❸ *Which group is greater in number, the fish or the dogs? Draw a line from each fish in the top group to a dog in the bottom group, and then draw a circle around the group that is greater than the other group.* **On the Back!** *Have students draw a group of red counters and a different number of yellow counters in a different group. Then have them draw a circle around the group that is greater than the other group.*

⭐**1**

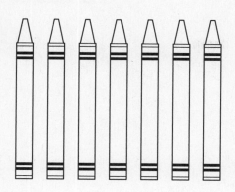

Ⓐ 5

Ⓑ 6

Ⓒ 7

Ⓓ 8

🍎**2**

Ⓐ △

Ⓑ △ △

Ⓒ △ △ △

Ⓓ △ △ △ △

🐟**3**

Directions Have students: ⭐ mark the number that tells how many crayons; 🍎 mark the picture that shows 4 shapes; 🐟 draw a group of buttons that is less in number than the group of buttons shown.

D 4·2

Name _____

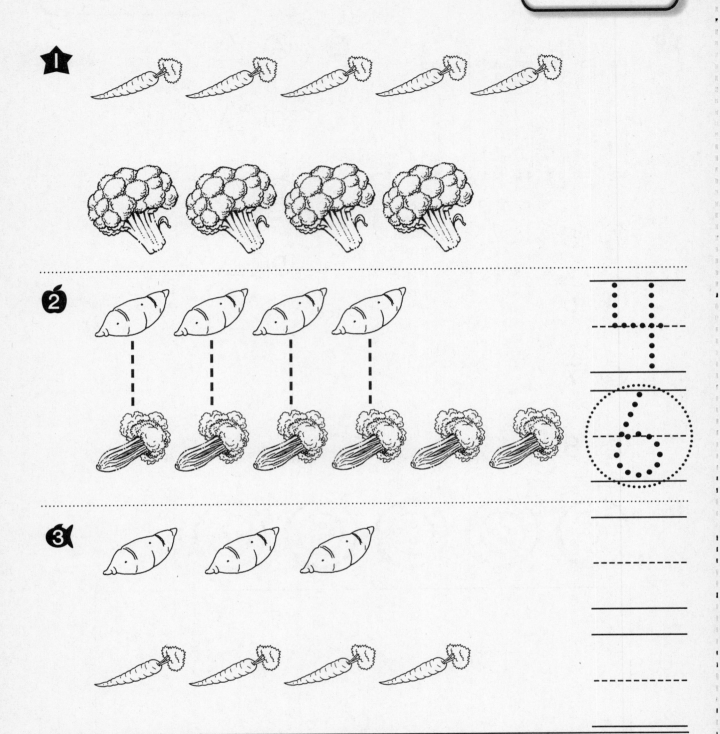

Directions Say: ⭐ *You can find out which number is greater by counting. Draw a line from each carrot on the top to a broccoli stalk on the bottom. There are not enough broccoli stalks to match each carrot, so the number of carrots is* **greater than** *the number of broccoli stalks. Count the number of objects in each group of vegetables, and then draw a circle around the group that is greater than the other group;* ❷ *How many sweet potatoes are there? How many celery stalks are there? Write the numbers that tell how many in each group. Which number is greater? Draw a circle around the number that is greater than the other number;* ❸ *Count the vegetables in each group, and then write the numbers that tell how many in each group. Compare the vegetables. Mark an X on the number that is less than the other number.*
On the Back! Have students draw a group of tomatoes and a group of onions, count them, write the numbers to tell how many in each group, and then mark an X on the number that is less than the other number.

Name _____

1

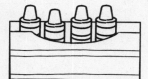

2

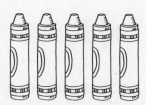

Directions Have students: **1** mark the picture that shows 6 ladybugs; **2** draw a circle around the group that shows a number of crayons that is greater than the number of crayons in the box.

D 4·3

Name _____

_____

- - - - - - - -

_____

_____

- - - - - - - -

_____

2

1 2 3 4 5 6 7 8 9 10

3

_____   _____

- - - - - - - -   - - - - - - - -

_____   _____

Directions Say: ⭐ *We use the words greater than and less than to compare groups of objects. How many black cubes are there? How many gray cubes are there? Write the numbers to tell how many. Draw lines to compare the cubes in each group, and then draw a circle around the number that is greater than the other number;* **2** *How many striped butterflies are there? How many gray butterflies are there? Write the numbers to tell how many, and then draw a circle around the number that is greater than the other number. Use the number sequence to help find the answer.* **3** *Have students count the stars, write the numbers to tell how many in each group, and then draw a circle around both numbers if they are equal, or mark an X on both numbers if they are NOT equal.* **On the Back!** *Have students draw two different groups of objects, write the numbers to tell how many, and then mark an X on the number that is less than the other number.*

R 4·3

Name _____

⭐1

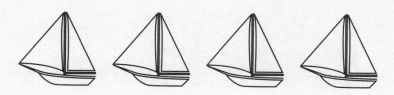

(A)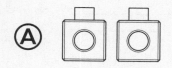

(B)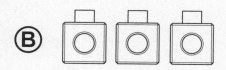

(C)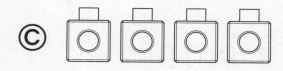

(D)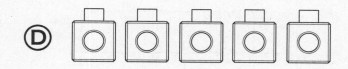

🍎2

_____

- - - - - - - - - - -

_____

Directions Have students: ⭐ mark the picture that shows the same number of cubes as boats; 🍎 count the number of fish in the tank, and then write the number that tells how many.

⭐ 1
_____
- - - - - - - - - -
_____
_____
- - - - - - - - - -
_____

🍎 2   5 · · · · · · · · · · · · · (7)

1 2 3 4 5 6 7 8 9 10

⭐ 3   5

      3

⭐ 4   7

      8

Directions ⭐ Say: *We can count objects to compare groups and tell whether the groups are* **equal** *or NOT equal. Look at the group of ducks. Let's count the gray ducks. Let's count the white ducks. Write the numbers to tell how many of each color duck. Draw a circle around both numbers if they are equal or mark an X on both numbers if they are NOT equal.* Have students: 🍎 *use the number sequence to show how they know which number is greater than the other number, and then draw a circle around the number that is greater;* ⭐ *draw counters in the ten-frames to show how they know which number is greater than the other number, and then draw a circle around the number that is greater;* ⭐ *draw pictures to show how they know which number is less than the other number, and then mark an X on the number that is less.* **On the Back!** Have students write two different numbers, and then draw pictures to show how they know which number is less than the other number. Then have them mark an X on the number that is less than the other number.

Play a Game

Partner Talk

Share your thinking while you work.

 **Start** Get 20 red squares.

Put ⓪ ① ② ③ ④ ⑤ ⑥ ⑦ ⑧ ⑨ in a 🛍.

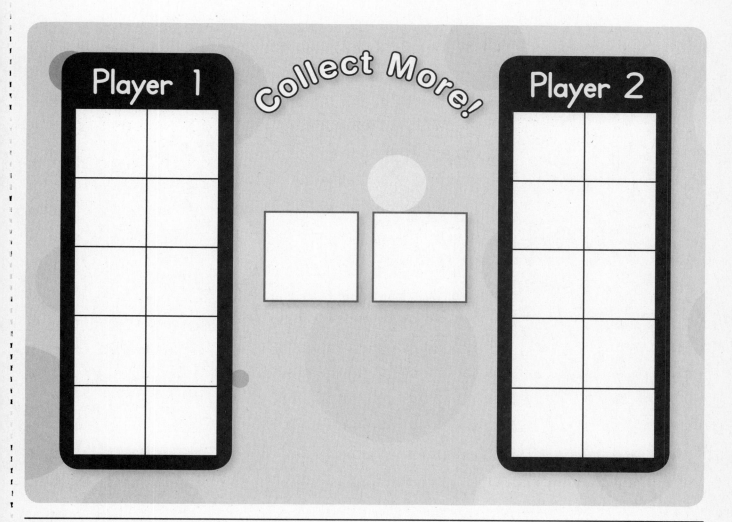

Player 1

Collect More!

Player 2

Materials	Number tiles 0–9, a bag for the tiles, 20 red squares
Oral Directions	**TRY** Give 10 red squares to one player. Give 10 red squares to the other player. Choose a game board. Each player picks a number tile from the bag. Put your tile in the tile space next to your game board. Put that many red squares on your game board. The player who has the greater number of squares on a game board keeps both tiles. Remove the squares. Play until the bag is empty. The player who collects more tiles wins.

TRY AGAIN If you have time, play again! This time, the player who has the number that is less keeps both tiles.

Play a Game

Partner Talk
Share your thinking while you work.

Start 🚶🚶 Get 20 red squares.

Put [0] [1] [2] [3] [4] [5] [6] [7] [8] [9] in a 🛍.

Get 10!

Player 1

Player 2

	Materials	Number tiles 0–9, a bag for the tiles, 20 red squares
	Oral Directions	**TRY** Give one game board to each player. Each player picks a tile from the bag. Put your tile in the tile space next to your game board. If you have the greater number, explain why. Put a square on your game board. Put the tiles back in the bag. Play until someone wins. The first player to get 10 squares wins.
		TRY AGAIN If you have time, play again! This time, the player with the number that is less collects a square.

(A) 7

(B) 8

(C) 9

(D) 10

❷

⭐⭐⭐⭐⭐

⭐⭐⭐⭐⭐⭐ ⭐⭐⭐⭐

Directions Have students: ❶ mark the number that tells how many stickers; ❷ draw a circle around the group of stars that is less in number than the group of stars in the box.

D 4•5

Copyright © Pearson Education, Inc., or its affiliates. All Rights Reserved. K

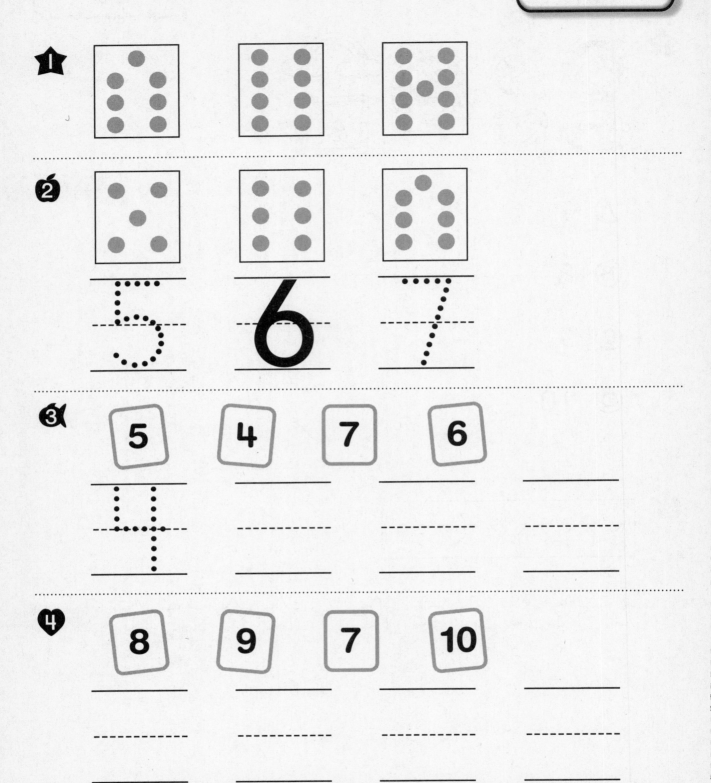

⭐1

2🍎

5   6   7

3❸
5   4   7   6

4💙
8   9   7   10

Directions Say: ⭐ **Count** the dots. Draw a circle around the box that shows 1 less than 8. Mark an X on the box that shows 1 greater than 8; 🍎 What number is 1 less than 6? Count the dots to help you, and then write the number. What number is 1 more than 6? Count the dots to help you, and then write the number; ❸ and 💙 Write the smallest number, and then count forward and write the number that is 1 greater than the number before. **On the Back!** Have students write a number, and then practice writing the numbers that are 1 less and 1 more than the number they wrote.

Play a Game

Start 👥 Get 18 red squares. Get 🎲.

NUMBER OF DOTS	COVER
4	4
Less than 4	←4
Greater than 4	4→

Materials 18 red squares, 1 dot cube

Oral Directions **TRY** Give 9 red squares to one player. Give 9 red squares to the other player. Choose a game board. Take turns. On your turn, toss the dot cube. Count the dots to find the number in all. Say the number. Follow the directions in the chart. If the number of dots you have is 4, put 1 square on the number 4. If the number of dots you have is less than 4, put 1 square on an arrow that shows less than 4. If the number of dots you have is greater than 4, put 1 square on an arrow that shows greater than 4. Take turns until one player wins. The first player to cover 9 game spaces wins.

TRY AGAIN If you have time, play again!

Play a Game

Share your thinking while you work.

Start 👫 Get 18 red squares. Get .

NUMBER OF DOTS	COVER
10	10
Less than 10	←10
Greater than 10	→10

Cover Nine

Cover Nine

Materials 18 red squares, 2 dot cubes

Oral Directions **TRY** Give 9 red squares to one player. Give 9 red squares to the other player. Choose a game board. Take turns. On your turn, toss the dot cubes. Count the dots to find the number in all. Say the number. Follow the directions in the chart. If the number of dots you have is 10, put 1 square on the number 10. If the number of dots you have is less than 10, put 1 square on an arrow that shows less than 10. If the number of dots you have is greater than 10, put 1 square on an arrow that shows greater than 10. Take turns until one player wins. The first player to cover 9 game spaces wins.

TRY AGAIN If you have time, play again!

Name _____

⭐ 1

Ⓐ ♡ ♡ ♡

Ⓑ ♡ ♡ ♡ ♡

Ⓒ ♡ ♡ ♡ ♡ ♡

Ⓓ ♡ ♡ ♡ ♡ ♡ ♡

- -

🍎 2

7		
	6	_____ _____ _____ _____
8		- - - - - - - - - - - - - - -
	5	_____ _____ _____ _____

- -

🐟 3

● ● ● ● ●   _____

● ●   - - - - - - -

                    _____

Directions Have students: ⭐ mark the picture that shows 3 hearts; 🍎 write the smallest number, and then count forward and write the number that is 1 greater than the number before; 🐟 draw more counters to make 10, and then write the number that tells how many.

D 4·6

Name _____

⭐ 1

2

3

4

Directions Say: ⭐ *Count the number of blocks. Draw a group of blocks that is 1 greater than the group of blocks shown;* 2 *Tasha sees some blocks on a rug. Then she adds 1 more. How many blocks are on the rug now?* Have students count the blocks, and then use reasoning to find the number that is 1 greater than the number of blocks shown. Have them draw counters to show the answer, and then write the number. Have students explain their reasoning. Say: *Use reasoning to find the number that is:* 3 *1 greater than the number of blocks shown. Draw counters to show the answer, and then write the number;* 4 *2 greater than the number of blocks shown. Draw counters to show the answer, and then write the number.* **On the Back!** Have students use connecting cubes to tell a story about 1 more or 2 more.

This book belongs to:

Sydney's Socks

Written by Nicole S. Rouse
Illustrated by Braj Gopal Sahoo

Sydney has socks everywhere!

Help Sydney sort her socks.

How many are ◇? ___

How many are NOT ◇? ___

Which group has more?

Topic 5   1

fold down

Color some of Sydney's socks.

Color the rest a different color.

How many are ☐? ___

How many are NOT ☐? ___

Sydney's socks are all sorted!

Topic 5   4

Help Sydney sort her socks.

How many are [sock] ? _____

How many are NOT [sock] ? _____

Which group has less?

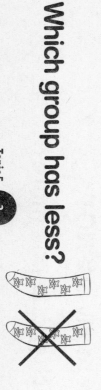

fold up

Help Sydney sort her socks.

How many are [sock] ? _____

How many are NOT [sock] ? _____

Which group has more?

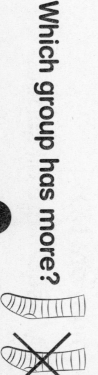

Name _____

Classify and Count Data

Topic 5 Standards

K.MD.B.3

See the front of the Student's Edition for complete standards.

Dear Family,

Your child is learning to sort objects into categories and count the objects in each group. He or she will use charts and tally marks to organize the information.

Classify Objects

Objects can be classified by sorting them into groups with similar characteristics. Crayons can be sorted by color.

Sort the crayons into categories: crayons that are green and crayons that are NOT green. Draw a circle around the crayons that are green. Mark an X on the crayons that are NOT green.

Here is an activity you can do with your child to understand classifying and counting objects.

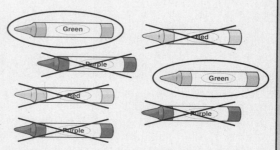

Red Squares or Blue Squares

Cut out 20 paper squares. Help your child color 10 squares red and 10 squares blue. (You can choose any 2 colors.) Have your child look for things in your house that are red and things that are blue. Each time he or she finds something that is red or blue, place that color square on the table in a row. At the end of the game, count how many of each color your child found. Ask, "Which color has a greater number of squares?"

Observe Your Child

Focus on Mathematical Practice 4:

Model with mathematics.

Help your child become proficient with Mathematical Practice 4. During the game, ask your child why you are placing the squares in two rows. Ask him or her to explain how placing the squares in rows makes it easier to figure out which group has more squares.

Nombre _____

Clasificar y contar datos

Estándares del Tema 5

K.MD.B.3

Los estándares completos se encuentran en las páginas preliminares del Libro del estudiante.

Estimada familia:

Su niño(a) está aprendiendo a agrupar objetos en categorías y a contar los objetos en cada grupo. Él o ella usará tablas y marcas de conteo para organizar la información.

Clasificar objetos

Los objetos se pueden clasificar al agruparlos por sus características similares. Los crayones se pueden agrupar por color.

Agrupa los crayones en categorías: crayones que son verdes y crayones que NO son verdes. Encierra en un círculo los crayones que son verdes. Escribe una X sobre los crayones que NO son verdes.

Esta es una actividad que puede hacer con su niño(a) para entender la clasificación y el conteo de objetos.

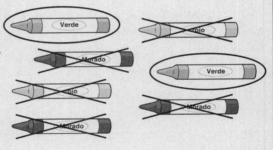

Cuadrados rojos o cuadrados azules

Recorte 20 cuadrados de papel. Ayude a su niño(a) a colorear 10 cuadrados de rojo y 10 cuadrados de azul. (Puede escoger 2 colores cualesquiera.) Deje que su niño(a) busque cosas en la casa que sean rojas y cosas que sean azules. Cada vez que encuentre algo que sea rojo o azul, coloque un cuadrado de ese color en una fila sobre la mesa. Al final del juego, cuente cuántos de cada color encontró su niño(a). Pregunte: "¿Qué color tiene un número mayor de cuadrados?"

Observe a su niño(a)

Enfoque en la Práctica matemática 4:
Representar con matemáticas.

Ayude a su niño(a) a adquirir competencia en la Práctica matemática 4. Durante el juego, pregunte a su niño(a) por qué coloca los cuadrados en dos filas. Pídale que explique cómo es que la colocación de los cuadrados en filas facilita calcular qué grupo tiene más fichas.

Name _____

Dogs

Directions Say: *Did you know that some dogs can be helpful to people? There are dogs that can help with hunting, farm work, and protecting the house. There are even dogs that can help people who are blind.* Have students sort the dogs into dogs that are: ❶ one color and dogs that are NOT one color, count them, and then write the numbers in the chart to tell how many. Then have students draw a circle around the category that is less in number than the other category and tell how they know; ❷ standing and dogs that are NOT standing, count them, and then write the numbers in the chart to tell how many. Then have students draw a circle around the category that is greater in number than the other category and tell how they know. **Extension** Have students draw a group of animals, sort them into two categories, write the numbers that tell how many, and then circle the group that is greater in number than the other group.

Name _____

Farm Animals

⭐

1   4   ✗ 9   yes   no

2   4   ✗ 9   yes   no

3   7   ✗ 6   yes   no

Directions Say: *Many different types of animals live on farms. Some farms just have sheep. Some farms just have turkeys. Some farms have many different types of animals, such as chickens, cows, horses, and pigs.* Have students listen to each problem, draw a circle around *yes* or *no*, and then use numbers, pictures, or words to explain their reasoning. Say: ⭐ *Jamal says that he counted 4 animals that are chickens and 9 animals that are NOT chickens. Does his answer make sense?* ❷ *Kasey says that she counted 4 animals that have feathers and 9 animals that do NOT have feathers. Does her answer make sense?* ❸ *Margie says that she counted 7 animals that have 4 feet and 6 animals that do NOT have 4 feet. Does her answer make sense?* **Extension** Have students draw up to 10 animals. Have them sort the animals, write the numbers that tell how many in each group, and then draw a circle around the number that is less than the other number.

Math and Science Activity   5·4

(A) 7

(B) 8

(C) 9

(D) 10

2

Directions Have students: ⭐ mark the number that tells how many ducks; 2 draw a circle around the group of animals that is greater in number than the other two groups of animals.

Directions ⭐ Say: *Objects can be sorted into* **categories.** *Categories group things by similar attributes. Look at the animals. One category is of animals that are birds. The other category is of animals that are NOT birds. Draw a circle around all of the birds.* Have students name the two categories of animals. Have them draw a circle around the: ❷ pets that are kittens, and then mark an X on the pets that are NOT kittens; ❸ turkeys that are white, and then mark an X on the turkeys that are NOT white; ❹ animals that have beaks, and then mark an X on the animals that do NOT have beaks. **On the Back!** Have students draw 7 animals, and then sort them into two categories.

Ⓐ 9

Ⓑ 8

Ⓒ 7

Ⓓ 6

_____

- - - - - - - - - - - - - - - - - -

_____

Directions Have students: ⬆ mark the number that tells how many shells; ② count the water bottles, and then practice writing the number that tells how many.

D 5-2

Directions Say: ⭐ *You can use a tally mark to show information. One tally mark stands for 1 object. How many ducks are gray? Let's count the tally marks for the gray ducks. How many ducks are NOT gray? Draw lines to show how many;* ② *You can record information in a chart. How many animals are in front of the barn? How many animals are NOT in front of the barn? Draw lines in the chart to show how many are in each category.* Have students draw lines in the chart as they count the animals in front of the barn and the animals that are NOT in front of the barn. Have them write the numbers to tell how many in each category in the other chart. ③ Have students draw lines in the chart as they count the butterflies that are on the flower and the butterflies that are NOT on the flower, and then write the numbers to tell how many in each category in the other chart. **On the Back!** Have students draw a group of circles, color some blue and some red, and then draw lines to show how many are in each category.

Name _____

 1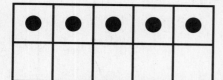

2

Ⓐ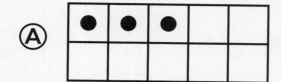

Ⓐ 2

Ⓑ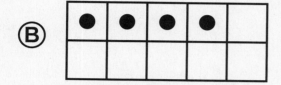

Ⓑ 3

Ⓒ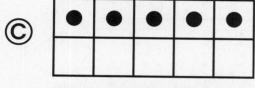

Ⓒ 4

Ⓓ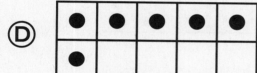

Ⓓ 5

3

Directions Have students: **1** mark the ten-frame that shows more counters than the ten-frame at the top; **2** mark the number that tells how many counters; **3** draw a group of books that is 1 greater than the group of books shown.

D 5·3

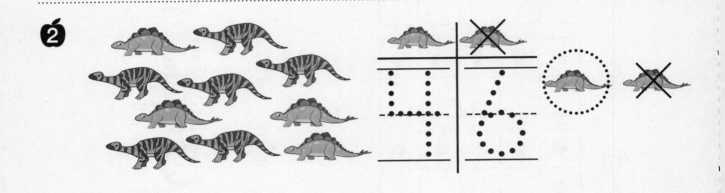

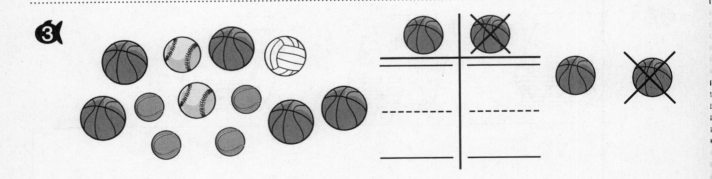

Directions Say: ⭐ *You can organize and show information in a* **chart.** *Look at the picture. Let's sort the animals into two categories. Count the animals that are frogs. Draw a line for each frog counted in the chart. Count the animals that are NOT frogs. Draw lines to show how many animals are NOT frogs in the chart;* ❷ *Let's sort the dinosaurs. How many dinosaurs have spikes? How many dinosaurs do NOT have spikes? Write the numbers to tell how many in each category. Have students draw a circle around the category that is less in number than the other category and tell how they know.* ❸ *Have students sort the balls into balls that are basketballs and balls that are NOT basketballs, count them, and then write the numbers in the chart to tell how many. Then have them draw a circle around the category that is greater in number than the other and tell how they know.* **On the Back!** *Have students draw a group of small squares. Then have them draw a group of large squares that is less in number than the group of small squares.*

Name _____

A

B

C

D

2

    A 0   **C** 2

    B 1   **D** 3

3

Directions Have students: **1** mark the picture that shows 8 swans; **2** mark the number that tells how many crayons there are in the box; **3** draw a group of buttons that is 2 greater than the group of buttons shown.

Name _____

⭐ _____
_____

_____

🍎 4   9   yes
(no)

⭐ 6   7   yes
no

❤ 6   7   yes
no

Directions Say: ⭐ *You can* **classify** *objects by sorting them into categories. Let's sort the cars into cars that are black and cars that are NOT black. How many cars are black? How many cars are NOT black? Write the numbers to tell how many;* 🍎 *Listen to this problem: Rebecca says that the category of black cars is greater in number than the category of cars that is NOT black. Does her answer make sense? Let's check. We counted 4 black cars and 9 cars that are NOT black. Is 4 greater than 9? Circle yes or no.* Have students listen to the problem, draw a circle around *yes* or *no,* and then use numbers, pictures, or words to explain their reasoning. Say: ⭐ *Marcus says that he counted 6 white cars and 7 cars that are NOT white. Does his answer make sense?* ❤ *April says that the category of white cars is less than the category of cars that is NOT white. Does her answer make sense?* **On the Back!** Have students draw and color up to 10 squares. Have them sort and count the squares, write the numbers that tell how many, and then draw a circle around the number that is less than the other number.

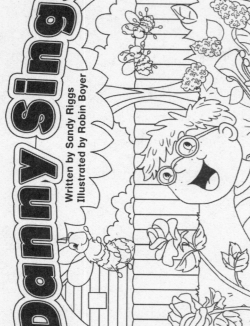

This book belongs to:

TOPIC
6
Story

Danny Sings

Written by Sandy Riggs
Illustrated by Robin Boyer

Danny sings about

things he sees.

He sees ____ large bee

and ____ small bees.

Danny sings about

3 bees.

Topic 6 **1**

---

fold down

Danny sees ____

yellow weeds.

He sees ____ purple

weeds.

Danny sings about

____ weeds.

Topic 6 **4**

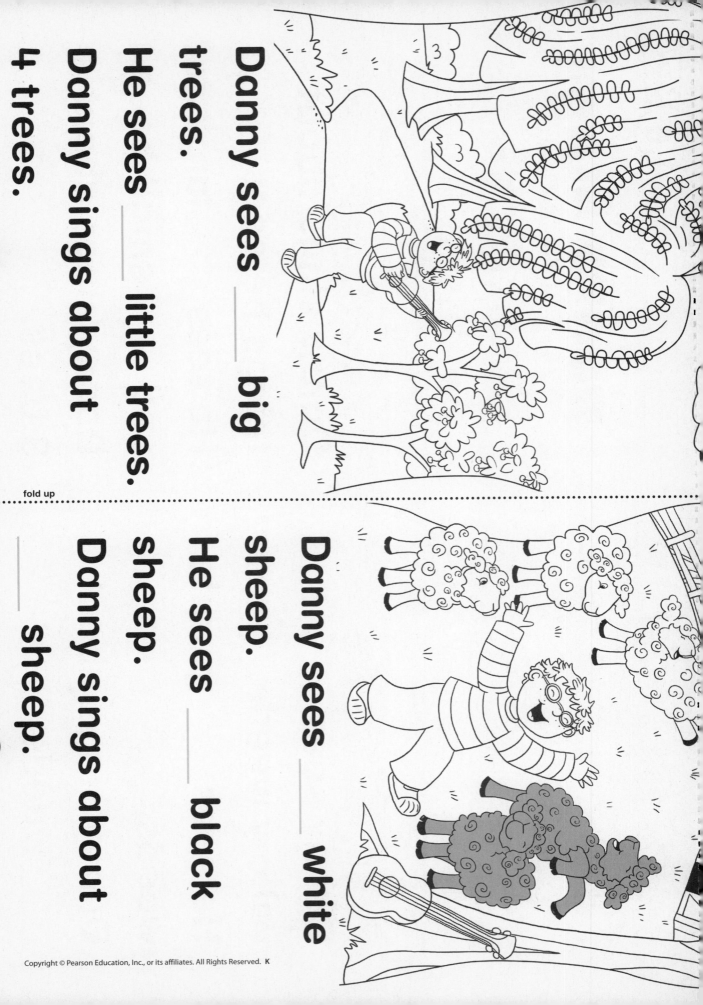

Danny sees ____ big trees.

He sees ____ little trees.

Danny sings about 4 trees.

fold up

Danny sees ____ white sheep.

He sees ____ black sheep.

Danny sings about ____ sheep.

Understand Addition

Topic 6 Standards
K.OA.A.1, K.OA.A.2, K.OA.A.5
See the front of the Student's Edition for complete standards.

Dear Family,

Your child is learning about addition. In this topic, he or she will learn to join two groups and decide how many there are in all. Your child will also learn to represent joining situations as equations using the symbols + and =.

Equations
Joining groups can be shown in an equation.

$3 + 5 = 8$

$5 + 3 = 8$

Here is an activity to do with your child to practice addition.

Stack the Pennies

Use 10 pennies. Count out 5 pennies and place them in a stack. Write "5 + " on a sheet of paper. Ask your child to add more pennies to your stack. Your child should count out the pennies (such as 4), and then place his or her group on your stack. Have your child write the number of pennies he or she added to your stack. Then work together to complete the equation: $5 + 4 = 9$. Reverse roles and continue the game.

Observe Your Child

Focus on Mathematical Practice 4:
Model with mathematics.

Help your child become proficient with Mathematical Practice 4. After you have completed an equation, ask your child to explain why 5 pennies and 4 pennies is 9 pennies, and is the same as $5 + 4 = 9$.

Nombre _____

Entender la suma

Estándares del Tema 6

K.OA.A.1, K.OA.A.2, K.OA.A.5

Los estándares completos se encuentran en las páginas preliminares del Libro
del estudiante.

Estimada familia:

Su niño(a) está aprendiendo sobre la suma. En este tema, aprenderá a juntar dos grupos
y decidir cuántos hay en total. Su niño(a) también aprenderá a representar situaciones en
las que se debe juntar grupos como ecuaciones usando los símbolos + y =.

Ecuaciones
La unión de grupos se puede mostrar en una ecuación.

$3 + 5 = 8$

$5 + 3 = 8$

Esta es una actividad que puede hacer con su niño(a) para practicar la suma.

Agrupar las monedas de 1¢

Use 10 monedas de 1¢. Cuente 5 monedas de 1¢ y colóquelas en una pila. Escriba "5 + "
en una hoja de papel. Pida a su niño(a) que añada más monedas de 1¢ a la pila. Su
niño(a) debería contar las monedas de 1¢ (por ejemplo, 4) y después colocar su grupo
en la pila. Pídale que escriba el número de monedas de 1¢ que añadió a la pila. Luego,
trabajen juntos para completar la ecuación: $5 + 4 = 9$. Intercambien roles y continúen
con el juego.

Observe a su niño(a)

Enfoque en la Práctica matemática 4
Representar usando las matemáticas.

Ayude a su niño(a) a adquirir competencia en la Práctica matemática 4. Después de
completar la ecuación, pida a su niño(a) que explique por qué 5 monedas de 1¢ y
4 monedas de 1¢ son igual a 9 monedas de 1¢, que es lo mismo que $5 + 4 = 9$.

Name _____

Baby Animals

1

_____ _____ _____

- - - - - - - -   - - - - - - - -   - - - - - - - -

_____ and _____ is _____ in all.

2

_____ _____ _____

- - - - - - - -   - - - - - - - -   - - - - - - - -

_____ and _____ is _____ in all.

Directions Say: *Did you know that some living things, such as dogs and cats, can have more than 1 baby at a time?*
Have students listen to the story, and then do all of the following to show each part to find how many in all: clap and
knock, hold up fingers, and give an explanation of a mental image. Ask them to color the number of each part, and then
write the number to tell how many in all. Say: **1** *Russell walks 2 puppies in the morning. He walks 3 puppies in the
afternoon. How many puppies does he walk in all?* **2** *A mother cow gets a drink of water. 2 baby calves get a drink of
water. How many animals drink water in all?* **Extension** Have students listen to the story, draw a picture to show what
is happening, and then write the number that tells how many in all. Say: *3 kittens play in a yard. Some kittens rest in the
yard. There are 7 kittens in all. How many kittens are resting?*

Name _____

Rocks

1

_____   _____   _____

---------- ◯ ---------- ◯ ----------

_____   _____   _____

2

_____   _____   _____

---------- ◯ ---------- ◯ ----------

_____   _____   _____

Directions Say: *Did you know that rocks do not have babies because they are not living things?* Have students listen to each story, add the groups of rocks, and then write an equation to show the addition. Say: **1** *Tyler has 3 rocks. He finds 4 rocks at the beach. How many rocks does Tyler have in all?* **2** *Allison has 6 rocks. Her sister gives her 2 rocks. How many rocks does Allison have in all?* **Extension** Have students listen to the story, draw a picture to show what is happening, and then write an equation. *Jessie has some rocks inside a box. She has 4 rocks outside the box. She has 9 rocks in all. How many rocks are inside the box?*

Math and Science Activity   **6·7**

1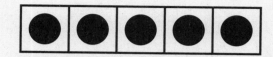

Ⓐ

Ⓑ

Ⓒ

Ⓓ

2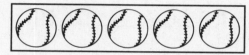

Ⓐ

Ⓑ

Ⓒ

Ⓓ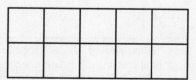

3

10

7

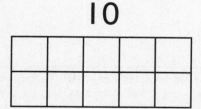

Directions Have students: ⭐ mark the picture that shows a group of counters that is less in number than the group of counters at the top; 🍎 mark the picture that shows 1 more baseball than the group of baseballs in the box; ⭐ draw counters in the ten-frames to show the numbers.

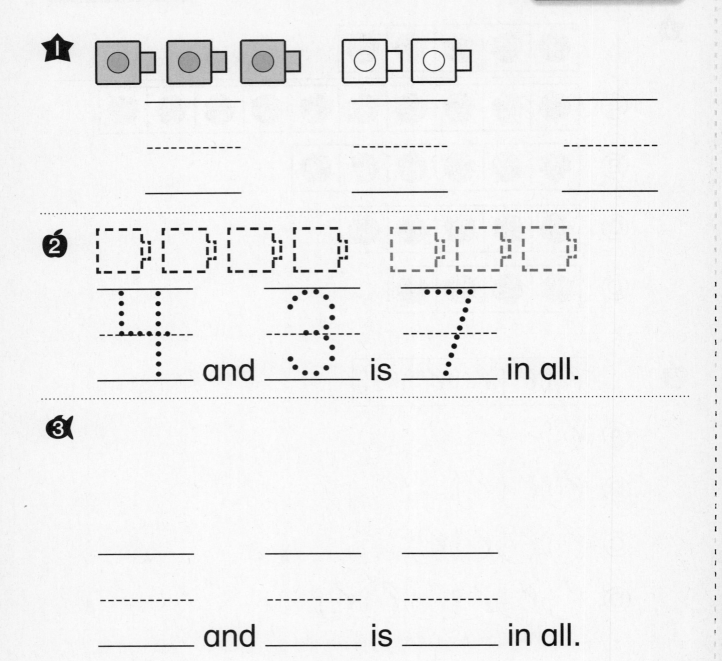

①

_____   _____   _____

- - - - - - - - - -   - - - - - - - - - -   - - - - - - - - - -

_____   _____   _____

②

_____ and _____ is _____ in all.

③

_____   _____   _____

- - - - - - - - - -   - - - - - - - - - -   - - - - - - - - - -

_____ and _____ is _____ in all.

Directions ① Say: *You can count the number of objects in a group to find how many there are **in all**. Let's count the cubes in each group. How many gray cubes are there? How many white cubes are there? Write the numbers to tell how many in each group. Now let's join the two groups and count all of the cubes. Write the number that tells how many in all.* Have students listen to the story, and then do all of the following to show each part to find how many in all: clap and knock, hold up fingers, and give an explanation of a mental image. Ask them to show how many of each color cube, and then write the number to tell how many in all. Say: **②** *Jason has 4 black cubes. He has 3 gray cubes. How many does he have in all?* **③** *Michelle has 5 blue cubes. She has 1 red cube. How many does she have in all?* **On the Back!** Have students draw a group of red cubes and a group of yellow cubes, and then write how many in each group and how many in all.

Name _____

⭐

Ⓐ 6

Ⓑ 7

Ⓒ 8

Ⓓ 9

🍎 2

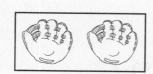

Ⓐ

Ⓑ

Ⓒ

Ⓓ

🐟 3

_____

– –

_____

Directions Have students: ⭐ mark the number that tells how many kangaroos; 🍎 mark the group that shows 2 more mitts than the group of mitts in the box; 🐟 count the buses, and then practice writing the number that tells how many.

Name _____

⭐ 1

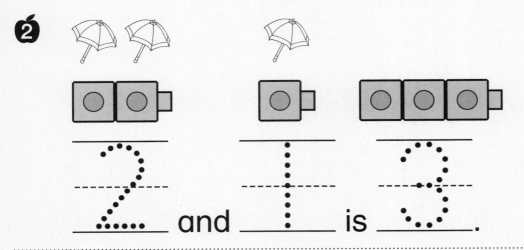

🍎 2

2 and ___ is 3.

🐟 3

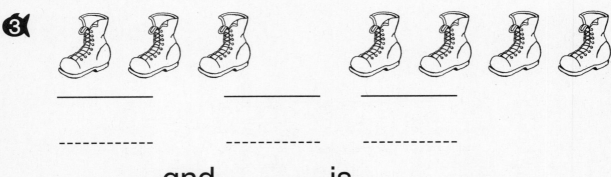

___ and ___ is ___.

Directions Say: ⭐ *Look at the boxes of shoes. When you find how many in all, you **join** two groups. Count the shoes in each box. Which box shows 4 shoes in all? Draw a circle around that box;* 🍎 *You can use connecting cubes to model adding to the group. Let's model the problem with connecting cubes. Use cubes to show the number of umbrellas in the first group, and then color that number of cubes. Show the number of umbrellas in the second group with cubes, and then color that number of cubes. Now, connect your cubes. How many cubes are there in all? Color that many cubes. Write an addition sentence that tells how many in all;* 🐟 *Use connecting cubes to model adding to the group, and then write an addition sentence that tells how many in all.* **On the Back!** Have students draw a group of up to 8 cubes. Then have them draw the number of cubes they need to add to equal 8, and then write a matching addition sentence.

Listen and Learn

Partner Talk

Share your thinking while you work.

Start 👥 Put ⌐1⌐ ⌐1⌐ ⌐2⌐ ⌐2⌐ ⌐3⌐ ⌐3⌐ ⌐4⌐ ⌐4⌐ ⌐5⌐ ⌐5⌐ in a 🛍.

Get 5 red squares.
Get 5 blue squares.

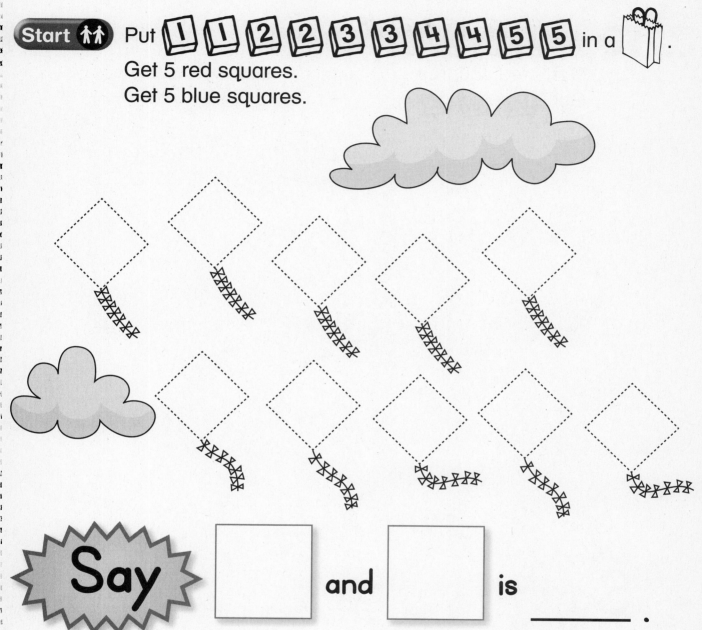

Say ☐ and ☐ is _____ .

Materials   Number tiles 1, 1, 2, 2, 3, 3, 4, 4, 5, 5, a bag for the tiles, 5 red squares, 5 blue squares

Oral Directions   **TRY** Pick a number tile from the bag. Put your number tile at the beginning of the sentence. Use that many red squares to make a group of flying kites. Ask your partner to pick a tile and put it in the second space in the sentence. Let your partner use blue squares to make a group with that many flying kites. Use your finger to trace around all the kites in both groups. Then say the sentence with the number of kites in each group and the number of kites in all. Let your partner trace around both groups of kites. Ask your partner to say the sentence too.

TRY AGAIN If you have time, remove the squares. Put the tiles back in the bag. Play again!

Listen and Learn

Start 👫 Put ⑤ ⑥ ⑦ ⑧ ⑨ in a 🛍.
Get 8 red squares.
Get 8 blue squares.

Say _____ and _____ is ☐.

Materials	Number tiles 5 – 9, a bag for the tiles, 8 red squares, 8 blue squares
Oral Directions	**TRY** Pick a number tile from the bag. Put that number tile in the space at the end of the sentence. Use red squares to make a group of flying kites. Make sure that the number of red kites is less than the number on the tile. Ask your partner to make another group of flying kites with blue squares until the number of kites in all is the number at the end of the sentence. Use your finger to trace around all the kites in both groups. Then say the sentence with the number of kites in each group and the number of kites in all. Let your partner trace around both groups of kites. Ask your partner to say the sentence too. **TRY AGAIN** If you have time, remove the squares. Put the tiles back in the bag. Play again!

Name _____

1 Ⓐ

Ⓑ

Ⓒ

Ⓓ

2

Ⓐ

Ⓑ

Ⓒ

Ⓓ

3

Directions Have students: **1** mark the picture that shows 6 raindrops; **2** mark the group with more buttons than the group in the box; **3** draw a group of counters that is less in number than the group of crabs shown.

D 6·3

Name _____

1

_____ _____ _____

_____ and _____ is _____ in all.

2

2 and 5 is 7.

3

_____ _____ _____

_____ and _____ is _____.

Directions Say: ★ Look at the groups of pigs. You can write an **addition sentence** to show how many in all. First, let's count the pigs in each group and write the numbers. Now let's join the two groups. Count how many, and then write the number that tells how many in all. Say the addition sentence aloud; **2** Look at the groups of animals. You can use counters to model putting groups together. How many frogs are in the first group? How many turtles are in the second group? Show the number of counters for each group of animals. Draw a circle around both groups to put them together. How many counters are there in all? Write an addition sentence that tells how many in all. **3** Have students draw a circle around the groups to put them together, write an addition sentence to tell how many in all, and then say the sentence aloud. **On the Back!** Have students tell a story where there are 8 animals in all. Have them draw counters to help solve the problem, and then write an addition sentence to tell the story.

R 6·3

Ⓐ 3 and 3 is 6.   Ⓒ 3 and 5 is 8.

Ⓑ 3 and 4 is 7.   Ⓓ 3 and 6 is 9.

_____   _____   _____

- - - - - - - -   - - - - - - -   - - - - - - -

_____ and _____ is _____.

_____

- - - - - - - -

_____

- - - - - - - -

_____

Directions Have students: mark the number sentence that tells how many soccer balls; ❷ listen to the story, and then do all of the following to show each part to find how many in all: clap and knock, hold up fingers, and give an explanation of a mental image. Ask them to draw and write the number of each part, and then write the number that tells how many in all. Say: *Nikki sees some black dogs playing in the park. She sees some gray dogs playing in the park. She sees 5 dogs in all;* ❸ count the kites in the group, draw a group of kites that is less than the group shown, and then write the numbers to tell how many.

1

3 and 3

3 ◯ 3

2

1 and 3

3

5 and 2

_____ _____

─────── ◯ ───────

_____ _____

Directions Say: **1** *When you add two groups together, you use the* **plus sign**. *Look at the picture. There are 3 trucks in one group. There are 3 trucks in the other group. 3 and 3 describes the problem. Write a plus sign in the circle to show that* 3 and 3 *is the same as* 3 + 3; **2** *How many trucks are in one group? Write the number that tells how many. How many trucks are in the other group? Write the number that tells how many. Write a plus sign to show adding the groups;* **3** *Count the buses in each group, and then write the numbers and the plus sign to show adding the groups.* **On the Back!** *Have students draw a picture to show adding two groups, and then write the numbers and the plus sign to show adding the groups.*

R 6·4

Helping Hands

Start 👥 Put  in a 🛍️.

Get 9 connecting cubes.

Materials	Number tiles 1, 1, 2, 2, 3, 3, 4, 4, and 5, paper bag, 9 connecting cubes
Oral Directions	**TRY** Take turns. Pretend your connecting cubes are towels. Pick a tile from the bag. Say that number. Put the tile in the first space. Count that number of cubes. Hang them on the top clothesline. Pick another tile. Say that number. Put that tile in the second space. Count that number of cubes. Hang them on the bottom clothesline. Ask your partner to say the first number *and* the second number. Pick up the cubes and join them together. Trace the plus sign when your partner says the word *and*. Count how many cubes you have in all. Say the number. Break the cubes apart and put the number tiles back in the bag. Take turns until each player gets four turns.

TRY AGAIN If you have time, play again! This time, begin with the second space and the bottom clothesline.

Helping Hands

Partner Talk

Share your thinking while you work.

Start 👫 Put ①①②②③③④④⑤ in a 🛍️.

Get 9 connecting cubes.

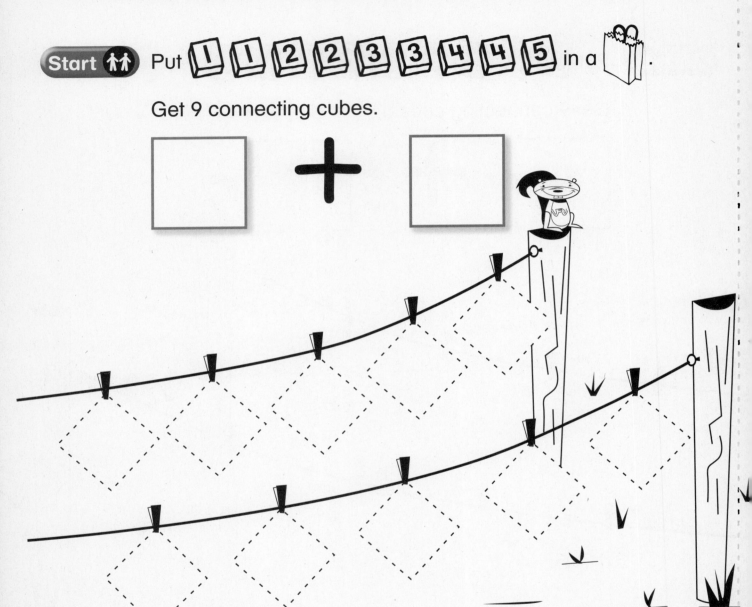

Materials	Number tiles 1, 1, 2, 2, 3, 3, 4, 4, and 5, paper bag, 9 connecting cubes
Oral Directions	**TRY** Take turns. Pretend your connecting cubes are towels. Pick a tile from the bag. Say that number. Put the tile in the first space. Count that number of cubes. Hang them on the top clothesline. Pick another tile. Say that number. Put that tile in the second space. Count that number of cubes. Hang them on the bottom clothesline. Ask your partner to say the first number *and* the second number. Pick up the cubes and join them together. Trace the plus sign when your partner says the word *and*. Count how many cubes you have in all. Say the number. Break the cubes apart. Ask your partner to use the same number tiles and switch their places. Repeat the same activity with the numbers in their new positions. Take turns until the bag of tiles is empty.
	TRY AGAIN If you have time, play again!

Name _____

1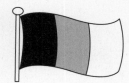

Ⓐ 0   Ⓒ 3

Ⓑ 1   Ⓓ 10

2

_____   _____   _____

- - - - - -   - - - - - -   - - - - - -

_____ and _____ is _____.

3

_____

- - - - - -

1 and 5 is _____.

Directions Have students: **1** mark the number that tells how many stars there are on the flag; **2** use counters to model putting together the groups, draw a circle around the groups to put them together, and then write an addition sentence to tell how many in all; **3** complete the addition sentence to tell how many in all.

D6·5

⭐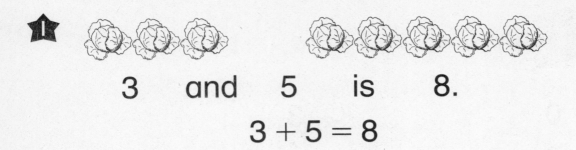

3   and   5   is   8.

3 + 5 = 8

🍎

5   and   l   is   6.

🐟

3   and   3   is   6.

_____   ⭕   _____   ⭕   _____

- - - - -   ⭕   - - - - -   ⭕   - - - - -

_____   _____   _____

Directions Say: ⭐ *When you add two groups, you can write an addition sentence that tells how many in all. You can use the **plus sign** and **equal sign** to write an addition equation that means the same thing. 3 and 5 is 8 can be written as 3 + 5 = 8. Draw a circle around the plus sign and mark an X on the equal sign;* 🍎 *How many ears of corn are there in the first group? How many ears of corn are in the second group? Add the groups to find the sum. You can use words to write an equation that tells the story. You can also use symbols to tell the story. Write the numbers, and then write a plus sign for the word* and, *and an equal sign for the word* is. *Read the equation;* 🐟 *Add the groups to find the sum, and then write an equation to show the addition.* **On the Back!** *Have students draw a picture to show adding two groups, and then write an equation to show the addition.*

Helping Hands

Start 👭 Put ⊡ ② ③ ④ ⑤ in a .

Get 9 red squares.

☐ **+** ☐ **=** _____

Materials   Number tiles 1–5, paper bag, 9 red squares

Oral Directions   **TRY** Pick a tile. Put it in the first space of the equation. Count that number of squares. Ask your partner to pick a tile, put it in the second space of the equation, and count that number of squares. Pretend your squares are pieces of cheese. Put all of the pieces of cheese on the plate. Find out how many there are in all. Say the sum. Use your finger to trace in the air. Trace the first number, then the plus sign, then the second number, then the equal sign, and then the sum. Trace the equation in the air three times. Watch as your partner traces the equation in the air three times.

TRY AGAIN If you have time, put the tiles back in the bag. Remove the squares. Play again!

Helping Hands

 Get [3] [4] [5] [6] [6] [7] [8] [9].

Get 12 red squares.

☐ + ☐ = **12**

Materials Number tiles 3, 4, 5, 6, 6, 7, 8, 9 and 12 red squares

Oral Directions **TRY** Pretend your squares are pieces of cheese. Ask your partner to put a number tile in the first space, and then put that number of pieces of cheese on the plate. Decide how many more pieces of cheese you need so that there will be 12 pieces of cheese on the plate in all. Put those pieces of cheese on the plate and show that number with a tile in the second space. Say the equation. Use your finger to trace in the air. Trace the first number, then the plus sign, then the second number, then the equal sign, and then the sum. Trace the equation in the air three times. Watch as your partner traces the equation in the air three times.

TRY AGAIN If you have time, remove the tiles and the squares. Play again!

1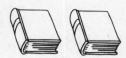

Ⓐ 2 and 2 is 4.
  $2 + 2 = 4$

Ⓑ 2 and 5 is 7.
  $2 + 5 = 7$

Ⓒ 5 and 5 is 10.
  $5 + 5 = 10$

Ⓓ 7 and 2 is 9.
  $7 + 2 = 9$

2

Ⓐ

Ⓑ

Ⓒ

Ⓓ

3

_____   _____

- - - - - - - ◯ - - - - - -

_____   _____

Directions Have students: **1** mark the addition sentence and equation that tells how many books in all; **2** mark the group that shows more shells than the group of shells in the box; **3** count the toys in each group, and then write the numbers and the plus sign to show adding the groups.

D 6·6

1

$$4 + 1 = 5$$

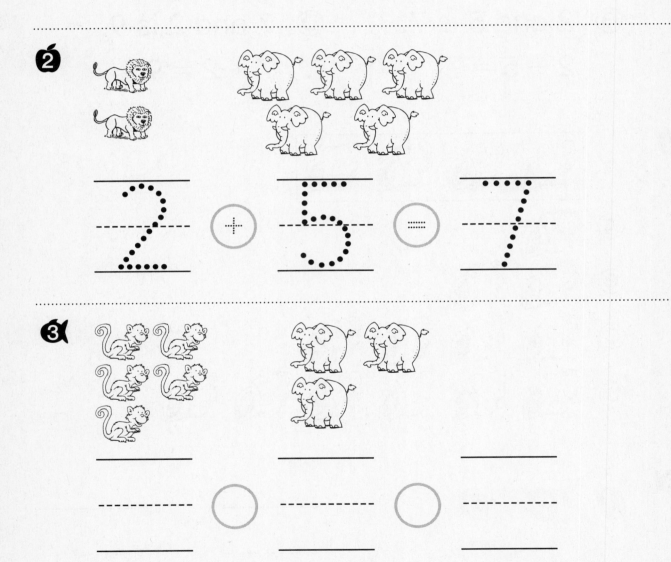

2

$$2 + 5 = 7$$

3

Directions Say: **1** *Draw a circle around the two groups of animals to put them together. You can use a plus sign and an equal sign to write an equation that tells how many **in all.** Draw a circle around the number that tells how many in all;* **2** *Look at the two groups of animals. How many lions are in the first group? How many elephants are in the second group? Write the numbers, the plus sign, and the equal sign to make an equation that tells how many in all. Read the equation.* **3** Have students add the group of monkeys to the group of elephants, and then write an equation to show the addition. **On the Back!** Have students draw a picture to show adding two groups, and then write an equation to show the addition.

Play a Game

Start 👥 Get 12 red squares.

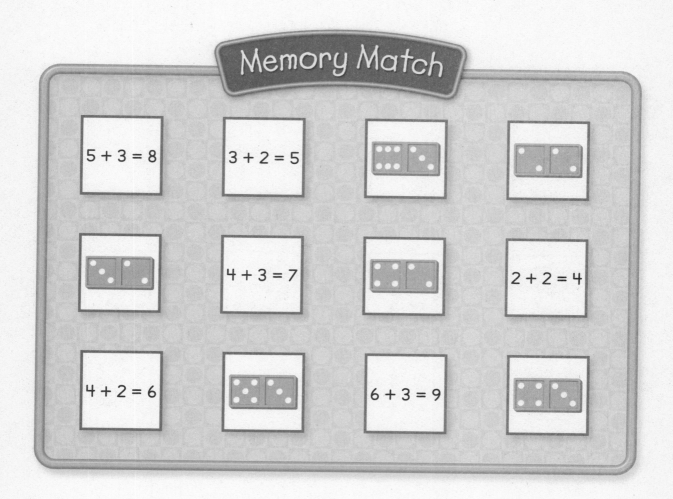

Memory Match

5 + 3 = 8	3 + 2 = 5
4 + 3 = 7	2 + 2 = 4
4 + 2 = 6	6 + 3 = 9

Materials 12 red squares

Oral Directions

TRY Before the game begins, cover each game space with a red square. Take turns. On your turn, uncover two game spaces. If you see an equation and a domino that matches the numbers in the equation, keep the squares. If not, put the squares back where they were. Play until all the spaces are uncovered. At the end of the game, count your squares. If you have more squares, you win.

TRY AGAIN If you have time, play again!

Play a Game

Start 👫 Get 12 red squares.

Memory Match

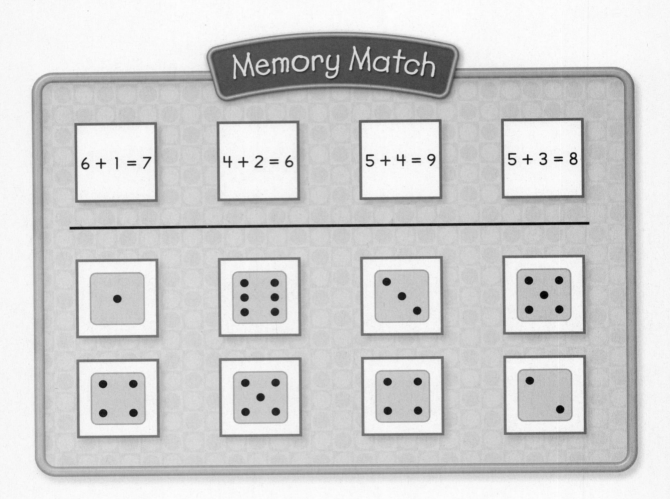

6 + 1 = 7	4 + 2 = 6	5 + 4 = 9	5 + 3 = 8

Materials   12 red squares

Oral Directions   **TRY** Before the game begins, cover each game space with a red square. Take turns. On your turn, uncover a game space above the line. Read the equation aloud to your partner. Uncover two game spaces below the line. If the pictures show two groups you can add with the numbers in your equation, keep the squares. If not, put the squares back where they were. Play until all the spaces are uncovered. At the end of the game, count your squares. If you have more squares, you win.

TRY AGAIN If you have time, play again!

Center Game ★★ 6·6

Name _____

⭐ 1

Ⓐ

Ⓒ

Ⓑ

Ⓓ

🍎 2

Ⓐ

Ⓑ

Ⓒ

Ⓓ

⭐ 3

_____

- - - - - - - - - - -

_____

Directions Have students: ⭐ mark the picture that shows 5 counters; 🍎 mark the group of trumpets that shows the same number of trumpets as the group in the box; ⭐ count the number of stars, and then write the number that tells how many.

Name _____

★1

_____   _____   _____

- - - - - -   ◯   - - - - - -   ◯   - - - - - -

_____   _____   _____

- -

②

_____   _____   _____

6   ⊕   ╎   ⊜   7

- - - - - -   - - - - - -   - - - - - -

❸

_____   _____   _____

- - - - - -   ◯   - - - - - -   ◯   - - - - - -

_____   _____   _____

Directions ★1 Say: _You can use counters to show addition, and then write an_ **equation** _to show the addition. How many counters do you need to show how many carrots are in the first group? The second group? How many carrots are there in all? Write the numbers to complete the equation._ Have students listen to the story, use counters to show the addition, draw a picture, and then write an equation to tell how many in all. Say: **②** _6 birds fly to the beach. 1 more joins them. How many birds fly to the beach in all? How many birds should you draw for the first group? The second group? How many counters do you need?_ **❸** _6 turtles are swimming. 3 more join them. How many turtles are there in all?_
On the Back! Have students draw a picture to show adding two groups, and then write an equation to show the addition.

R 6·7

Name _____

 1

_____

Ⓐ

Ⓑ

Ⓒ

Ⓓ

2

_____

- - - - - - - - - -

_____

3

_____

- - - - - - - - - -

_____

Directions Have students: **1** mark the necklace with the same number of beads as the necklace at the top; **2** count the cows, and then write the number that tells how many; **3** count the dolphins, and then write the number that tells how many.

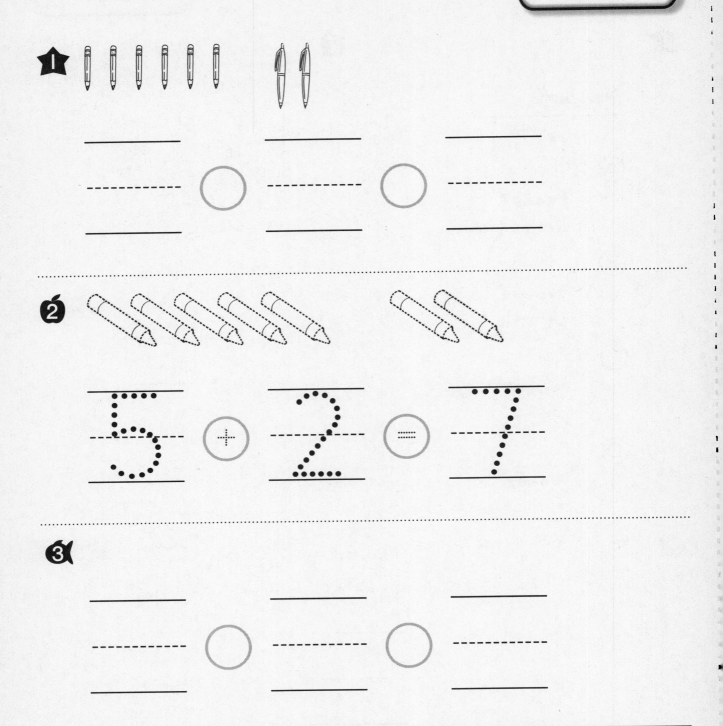

1

2

$$5 + 2 = 7$$

3

Directions Say: **1** *An equation uses a plus sign to* **add** *and an equal sign to show how many there are in all. Let's add these two groups of school supplies. How many pencils are in the first group? How many pens are in the second group? How many school supplies are there in all? Write an equation to show the addition;* **2** *You can draw pictures to show what is happening in a story problem. Listen to this story: Luz has 5 blue crayons and 2 purple crayons. How many crayons does she have in all? Draw crayons to show how many Luz has. How many blue crayons should you draw? How many purple crayons? Now, count how many there are in all. Write an equation that matches the problem;* **3** *Listen to the story, draw a picture to show what is happening, and then write an equation. There are 6 pencils on a desk. Joey puts 3 erasers on the desk. How many school supplies are there in all?* Have students explain their work. **On the Back!** Have students draw a picture to show what is happening in the equation $4 + 3 = 7$.

Name _____

1

(A) $5 + 2 = 7$

(B) $6 + 1 = 7$

(C) $5 + 3 = 8$

(D) $6 + 2 = 8$

2

(A) $4 + 4 = 8$

(B) $5 + 2 = 7$

(C) $4 + 3 = 7$

(D) $3 + 3 = 6$

3

_____   _____   _____

----------- + ---------- = -----------

_____   _____   _____

Directions Have students: **1** and **2** mark the equation that matches the picture; **3** complete the equation that tells about adding the groups of penguins.

1 ◯ ◯ ◯ ◯ ●

_____ _____ _____

- - - - - ◯ - - - - - ◯ - - - - -

_____   _____

2 ◯ ◯ ◯ ● ●

3 ⊕ 2 ⊜ 5

3 ◯ ◯ ◯ ◯ ◯

2 ◯ - - - - ◯ - - - -

4 ◯ ◯ ◯ ◯ ◯

_____ _____ _____

- - - - - ◯ - - - - - ◯ - - - - -

_____   _____

Directions Say: **1** *You can write an* **equation** *to show what is happening in a picture. How many counters are white? How many counters are black? Write an equation to match the counters;* **2** *The counters show a different way to make 5. How many counters are white? How many counters are black? Complete the equation to match the counters.* **3** *and* **4** *Have students color the counters to complete the pattern of different ways to make 5, and then write an equation to match the counters.* **On the Back!** *Have students draw pictures to show three different ways to make 4.*

Try Together

Partner Talk

Share your thinking while you work.

Start 👫 Get .

Get 4 red squares.
Get 4 blue squares.

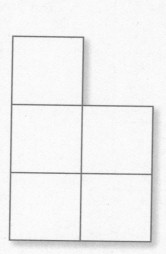

  **Say** ▢ + ▢ = 5

Materials   Number tiles 1–4, 4 red squares, 4 blue squares

Oral Directions   **TRY** Take turns. Choose any number tile. Put that number of red squares in the tower. Put the tile at the beginning of the equation to show how many squares you put in the tower. Ask your partner to use blue squares to finish building the tower. Put a tile in the second space in the equation to show the number of squares your partner used to finish the tower. Count all the squares in the tower. Take turns reading the equation and explaining what the equation means. Remove the squares and the number tiles.

TRY AGAIN If you have time, play again! This time, begin with the blue squares.

Try Together

Start  Get ⊡ ② ③ ④ ⑤ ⑤ ⑥ ⑦ ⑧ ⑨.

Get 9 red squares.
Get 9 blue squares.

 **Say** ☐ + ☐ = **10**

Materials Number tiles 1–9, and another 5 tile, 9 red squares, 9 blue squares

Oral Directions **TRY** Choose any number tile and put it in the first space of the equation. Put that number of red squares in the tower. Ask your partner to use blue squares to finish building the tower. Put a tile in the second space of the equation to show the number of squares your partner used to finish the tower. Count all the squares in the tower. Take turns reading the equation and explaining what two groups were added together. Remove the squares and the number tiles. Take turns until all of the tiles have been used.

TRY AGAIN If you have time, play again! This time, begin with the blue squares.

Name _____

 1

Ⓐ $4 + 3 = 7$ Ⓒ $3 + 2 = 5$

Ⓑ $4 + 2 = 6$ Ⓓ $2 + 3 = 5$

2

8

Ⓐ 10

Ⓑ 9

Ⓒ 8

Ⓓ 7

3

_____ _____ _____

---------- + ---------- = ----------

_____ _____ _____

Directions Have students: **1** mark the equation that tells how many planes there are in all; **2** mark the number that is less than the number at the top; **3** write an equation that tells how many flamingos there are in all.

D 6·10

1

5 + 3 = 8

2

◯ ◯ ◯ ◯ ◯

4 + 1 = 5

 3

___ ___ ___

------ + ------ = ------

___ ___ ___

Directions **1** Say: *You can write an equation to match a story problem. Listen to this story: There are 5 pears in a basket and 3 pears outside of the basket. Look at the equation. It has a plus sign, equal sign, and a* **sum.** *The sum tells you how many in all. Draw a circle around the sum. Have students listen to the story. Say:* **2** *There are 4 apples in a basket and 1 apple outside of the basket. How many apples are there in all? Let's draw 4 counters to show the apples inside the basket. Now, draw 1 more counter to show the apple outside of the basket. Count the counters. Write an equation that tells how many there are in all;* **3** *Tom picked 7 tomatoes and then picked 2 tomatoes. How many tomatoes does he have in all? Draw a picture to show what is happening, write an equation, and then explain your answer.* **On the Back!** *Ask students to tell an addition story. Have them draw a picture to show what is happening, write an equation, and then explain their answer.*

Listen and Learn

Partner Talk

Share your thinking while you work.

Start 👫 Get ①②③④⑤⑥⑦. Get a 🎲.

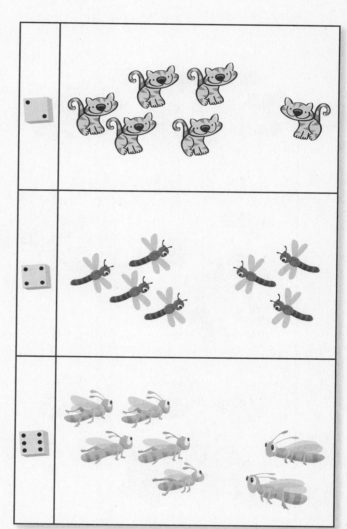

_____ **+** _____ **=** _____

Materials	Number tiles 1 – 7, 1 dot cube
Oral Directions	**TRY** Take turns. Toss the cube. Find the picture next to that number of dots. Tell an addition story about that picture. Ask your partner to use number tiles in the spaces below the pictures to model the number in each group and how many in all. Say the equation that you modeled. Remove the tiles.
	TRY AGAIN If you have time, take turns telling your own addition stories.

Center Game ★ **6·10**

Listen and Learn

Start 👥 Get [1] [2] [3] [4] [5] [6] [7] [8] [9]. Get a .

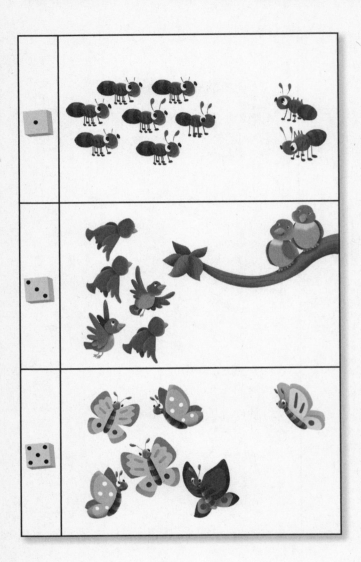

_____ + _____ = _____

Materials Number tiles 1 – 9, 1 dot cube

Oral Directions   **TRY** Take turns. Toss the cube. Find the picture next to that number of dots. Tell an addition story about that picture. Ask your partner to use number tiles in the spaces below the pictures to show the number in each group and how many in all. Say the equation that you modeled. Remove the tiles.

TRY AGAIN If you have time, take turns telling your own addition stories.

This book belongs to:

Where's My Fish?

Written by Al Cohen
Illustrated by Robin Boyer

Zak has 4 fish.

Maria wants a fish.

So Zak gives her 1 fish.

Now Zak has

1 2 3 4 5 6 fish.

Topic 7 **1**

---

fold down

Zak, Maria, and Ben

meet to eat.

Together they have

1 2 3 4 5 6 fish! But

Sara has only a worm.

Topic 7 **4**

Ben wants a fish.

So Zak gives him 1 fish.

Now Zak

has 1 2 3 4 5 6 fish.

fold down

Then Sara flies away

with 1 fish.

It falls deep into the lake.

Now Zak only

has 1 2 3 4 5 6 fish!

Name _____

Understand Subtraction

Topic 7 Standards
K.OA.A.1, K.OA.A.2, K.OA.A.5
See the front of the Student's Edition for complete standards.

Dear Family,

Your child is learning about subtraction. He or she will learn to understand subtraction as taking apart a quantity of objects and separating them into two separate groups and as taking away a quantity of objects from a group. Your child will also learn to represent take-away situations as equations using the symbols − and =.

Take Apart
Separate a set of objects into two groups.

6 take away 2 is 4.

Practice these skills with your child by using the following activity.

What's in the Bag?

Gather 8 to 10 small objects. Count the objects as you place them in a paper bag, basket, or box. Take out 4 objects and ask your child how many objects are left. Help him or her write the equation to explain the action on a sheet of paper. (8 − 4 = 4) Reverse roles, and continue the game by varying the number of total objects.

Observe Your Child

Focus on Mathematical Practice 4:
Model with mathematics.

Help your child become proficient with Mathematical Practice 4. During one of your turns use the sentence stem: ____ take away ____ is ____. Then have your child write a matching equation.

Nombre _____

Entender la resta

Estándares del Tema 7
K.OA.A.1, K.OA.A.2, K.OA.A.5

Los estándares completos se encuentran en las páginas preliminares del Libro del estudiante.

Estimada familia:

Su niño(a) está aprendiendo sobre la resta. Él o ella aprenderá a entender la resta como la separación de una cantidad de objetos en dos grupos diferentes y también como quitar objetos de un grupo. Su niño(a) también aprenderá a representar situaciones sobre quitar usando ecuaciones que tengan los símbolos $-$ y $=$.

Quitar
Separe un grupo de objetos en dos grupos.

Si a 6 se le quitan 2, son 4.

Practique estas destrezas con su niño(a) usando la siguiente actividad.

¿Qué hay en la bolsa?

Busque de 8 a 10 objetos pequeños. Cuente los objetos mientras los coloca en una bolsa de papel, canasta o caja. Saque 4 objetos y pregunte a su niño(a) cuántos objetos quedan. Ayúdele a escribir una ecuación para explicar la acción en una hoja de papel. $(8 - 4 = 4)$ Invierta los papeles y continúe el juego cambiando el número de objetos en total.

Observar a su niño(a)

Enfoque en la Práctica matemática 4
Representar usando las matemáticas.

Ayude a su niño(a) a adquirir competencia en la Práctica matemática 4. En alguno de sus turnos use el fragmento de oración: si a _____ le quito _____, me quedan _____; y pida a su niño(a) que escriba una ecuación que lo represente.

Animal Needs

1

6 take away 3 is 3.

_____   _____   _____

- - - - - - - - - ◯ - - - - - - - ◯ - - - - - - - -

_____   _____   _____

2

9 take away 5 is 4.

_____   _____   _____

- - - - - - - - - ◯ - - - - - - - ◯ - - - - - - - -

_____   _____   _____

3

4 take away 1 is 3.

_____   _____   _____

- - - - - - - - - ◯ - - - - - - - ◯ - - - - - - - -

_____   _____   _____

Directions Say: *Animals have different kinds of needs. They need food, water and shelter for survival.* **1**–**3** Have students use counters to model the problem, mark Xs to subtract, and then write an equation to find the difference. **Extension** Have students listen to the story, draw a picture to show what is happening, and then write an equation that tells how many are left. Say: *There are 9 puddles of water. The sun dried up 3 puddles. There are 6 puddles left.*

Name _____

More Animal Needs

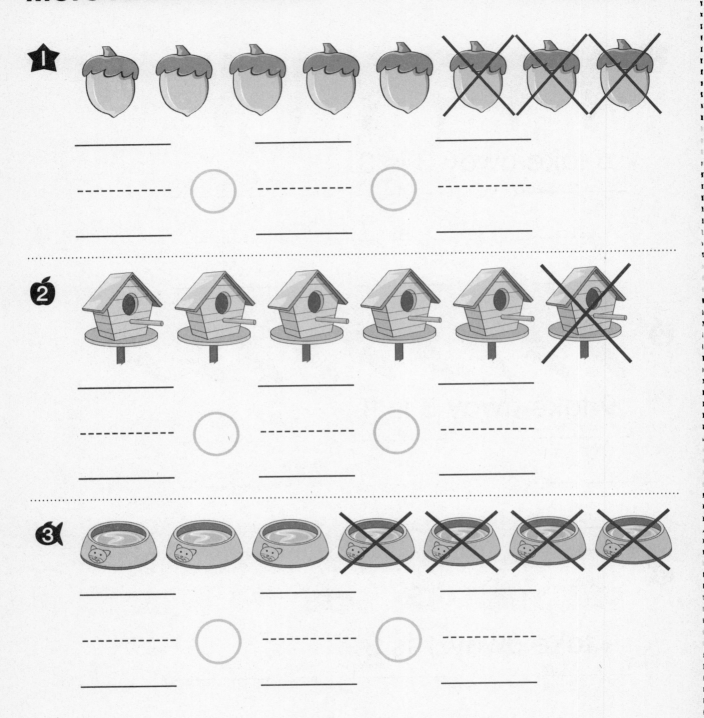

Directions Say: *Animals have different kinds of needs. Some animals eat meat, other animals eat seeds, grains or nuts.*
All animals need water. Animals also need to have a place to live such as an ocean, nest or tree. ❶–❸ Have students
use counters to model the problem, and then write an equation to tell how many are left. **Extension** Have students listen
to the story, draw a picture to show what is happening, and then write an equation that tells how many are left. Say: *There*
are 8 ears of corn in a field. A squirrel eats 2 of them. How many ears of corn are left?

⭐ 1

Ⓐ 4 + 3

Ⓑ 3 + 6

Ⓒ 3 + 3

Ⓓ 3 + 5

🍎 2 ☆☆☆☆☆☆☆☆☆

10   9   7   6

Ⓐ   Ⓑ   Ⓒ   Ⓓ

⭐ 3

_____

- - - - - - - - - -

_____

Directions Have students: ⭐ mark the addition that shows adding the two groups of boats; 🍎 mark the number that tells how many stars; ⭐ count the paper clips, and then write the number that tells how many.

Name _____

 1

_____

- - - - - - - - - -

_____ in all

---

2 **8** in all 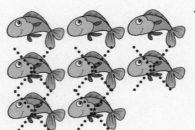 _____ are left.

---

3 **5** in all  _____

- - - - - - - - - -

_____ are left.

---

4 9 in all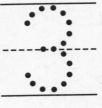

_____

- - - - - - - - - -

_____ are left.

Directions Say: **1** *Look at the picture. You can count objects to find how many there are in all. Let's count the frogs. Write the number that tells how many in all;* **2** *Look at the picture. What number tells how many fish in all? Mark an X on 5 fish. How many fish do NOT have an X on them? So, there are 3 fish left. Write the number that tells how many fish are left.* Have students listen to the story, and then do all of the following to find how many are left: give an explanation of a mental image, use objects to act it out, and hold up fingers. Have them mark an X on how many swim away, and then write the numbers to tell how many are left. Say: **3** *5 fish swim near a rock. 1 swims away. How many fish are left?* **4** *9 turtles swim in a lake. 4 swim away. How many turtles are left?* **On the Back!** Have students draw 8 circles. Have them mark an X on some of them, and then write the number to tell how many circles are left.

Look and See

Start 👥 Put 0 1 2 3 4 5 6 7 8 9 in a .

Get 9 squares.

Take away ☐ . _____ are left.

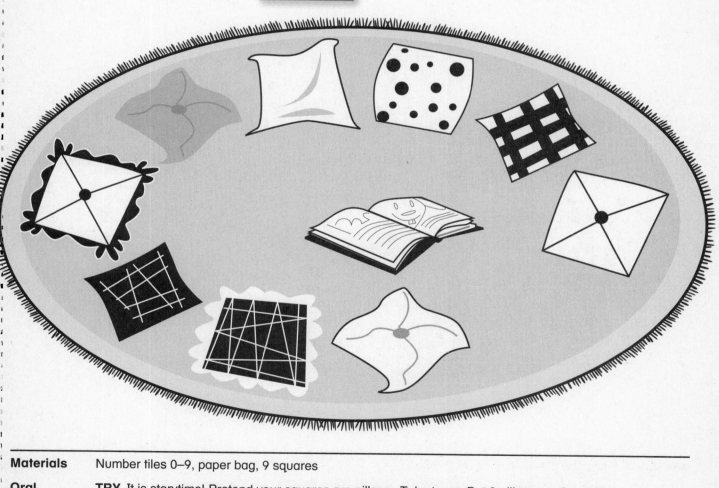

Materials	Number tiles 0–9, paper bag, 9 squares
Oral Directions	**TRY** It is storytime! Pretend your squares are pillows. Take turns. Put 9 pillows on the rug. On your turn, pick a tile from the bag. Put it in the space above the rug. Take away that number of pillows. Tell how many pillows are left. Ask your partner to trace that number in the air. Remove the squares. Set the tile aside. Take turns until the bag is empty.

TRY AGAIN If you have time, play again! |

Look and See

 Put 0 1 2 3 4 5 6 7 8 9 in a .

Get 9 squares.

Put
your tile
here.

Materials	Number tiles 0–9, paper bag, 9 squares
Oral Directions	**TRY** It is storytime! Pretend your squares are pillows. Take turns. Put 9 pillows on the rug. Then pick a tile from the bag. Put it in the space above the rug. Take some pillows off the rug, but leave your number of pillows on the rug. Ask your partner to tell how many pillows you took away, and to trace that number in the air. Remove the squares. Take turns until the bag of tiles is empty.
	TRY AGAIN If you have time, play again!

Name _____

1

10	9	8	7
Ⓐ	Ⓑ	Ⓒ	Ⓓ

2

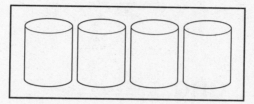

Ⓐ 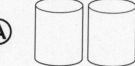   Ⓒ

Ⓑ 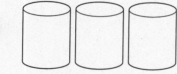   Ⓓ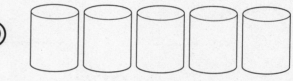

3

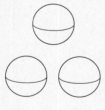   

_____   _____   _____

---------- **+** ---------- **=** ----------

_____   _____   _____

Directions Have students: **1** mark the number that tells how many paintbrushes; **2** mark the group of cans that is greater in number than the group of cans in the box; **3** write the numbers that tell how many of each group of toys, and then write the sum to complete the equation.

D 7·2

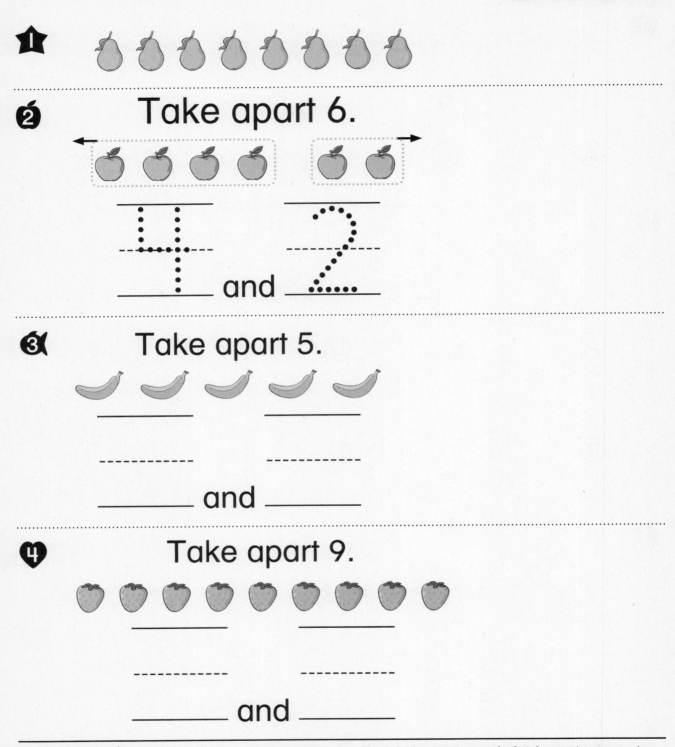

1.

2. Take apart 6.

4 and 2

3. Take apart 5.

_____ and _____

4. Take apart 9.

_____ and _____

Directions Say: 1. *When you **separate** groups, you take the objects in the group apart. Let's take apart, or separate, the pears. Draw a circle around the first 4 pears. Draw a circle around the last 4 pears. How many are in each group?* 2. *Take apart the group of apples. First, draw a circle around a group of apples. How many are in that group? Draw a circle around a second group of apples. How many are in that group? Write the numbers to tell the parts.* 3. *and* 4. *Have students take apart the group of fruit. Then have them draw a circle around the parts they made, and then write the number to tell the parts.* **On the Back!** *Have students draw a group of 7 oranges. Have them take apart the group, draw a circle around the parts they made, and then write the numbers to tell the parts.*

R 7-2

Name _____

Ⓐ 2 and 2 is 4.   Ⓒ 2 and 1 is 3.

Ⓑ 3 and 2 is 5.   Ⓓ 3 and 1 is 4.

2

Ⓐ    Ⓒ

Ⓑ 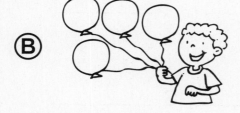   Ⓓ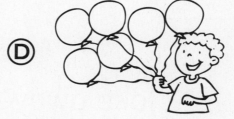

 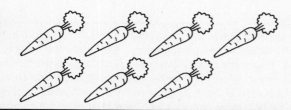

_____

- - - - - - - - -

_____

Directions Have students: **1** mark the addition sentence that matches the picture; **2** mark the picture that shows the boy with the same number of balloons as the girl; **3** write the number that tells how many carrots.

Name _____

⭐ **7 in all** _____

⬤ ⬤ ⬤ ⬤ ⊗ ⊗ ⊗ _____ are left.

2 ⬤ ⬤ ⬤ ⊗ ⊗

5 take away 2 is 3 .

3 ⬤ ⬤ ⬤ ⬤

_____ take away _____ is _____ .

Directions Say: ⭐ *When you mark an X, or take away, objects in a group, you count the objects that do NOT have Xs to find how many are* **left.** *How many counters are marked with Xs? How many counters are left? Write the number to tell how many are left;* **2** *Listen to this story: Lauri has 5 counters. She takes away 2 counters. How many are left? Write the number of counters Lauri started with. How many did she take away? Mark an X on the counters to show how many Lauri takes away, and then write that number. Count the counters that do NOT have Xs. How many are left? Write that number. Now read the sentence;* **3** *Listen to the story, mark Xs to show how many to take away, and then write the numbers to complete the sentence: Jeff has 4 counters. He takes away 3 counters. How many are left?* **On the Back!** *Have students draw counters to tell a take-away story, and then have them write the take-away sentence.*

Helping Hands

Start 👬 Put ❘ 2 3 4 5 6 in a 🛍.

Get 6 red squares.

Materials	Number tiles 1–6, a bag for the tiles, 6 red squares
Oral Directions	**TRY** Take turns. Put 6 red squares on the strip at the top of the page. Count them aloud as you put them there. Pretend your squares are stamps. Pick a tile from the bag. Take that number of stamps from the strip, and then put each one on an envelope. Say, "6 take away ☐ is __." Ask your partner to say it again. Set the tile aside. Remove your squares and place them on the strip. Repeat until the bag of tiles is empty.
	TRY AGAIN Put the tiles back in the bag. Play again!

Helping Hands

Start 👥 Put [1] [2] [3] [4] [5] [6] [7] [8] [9] in a 🛍️.

Get 9 red squares.

Materials	Number tiles 1–9, a bag for the tiles, 9 red squares
Oral Directions	**TRY** Take turns. Put 9 red squares in the spaces at the top of the page on the left. Count them aloud as you put them there. Pretend your squares are stamps. Pick a tile from the bag. Take that number of stamps, and put each one on an envelope. Say, "9 take away ☐ is __." Ask your partner to say it again. Set the tile aside. Remove your squares and place them in the spaces at the top of the page. Repeat until the bag of tiles is empty.
	TRY AGAIN Put the tiles back in the bag. Play again!

Name _____

⭐①

8

Ⓐ 7

Ⓑ 8

Ⓒ 9

Ⓓ 10

②

Ⓐ 7

Ⓑ 6

Ⓒ 3

Ⓓ 1

⭐③

_____   _____   _____

_____ take away _____ is _____ .

Directions Have students: ⭐① mark the number that is less than the number on the card; ② mark the number that tells how many lemons are left on the tree; ⭐③ look at the picture, and then write the numbers to complete the sentence.

D 7·4

1

9 take away 4

9 ◯ 4

2

6 take away 5

3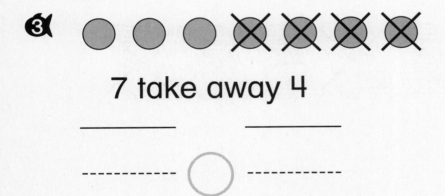

7 take away 4

_____   _____

- - - - - ◯ - - - - -

_____   _____

Directions Say: **1** *When you take away some objects from a group, you subtract. You can use a **minus sign** to show subtraction. Listen to this problem: There are 9 counters. 4 counters are subtracted, or taken away. 9 take away 4 describes the problem. Write a minus sign in the circle to show that 9 take away 4 is the same as 9 − 4;* **2** *You can use a picture to show subtraction. Let's count how many counters there are in all. Write that number on the first line, and then write the minus sign in the circle. Now count how many counters are taken away. Write that number on the second line. 6 − 5 means the same as 6 take away 5;* **3** *Count the counters and write the number that tells how many, and then write the minus sign and the number subtracted.* **On the Back!** *Have students draw counters to show 8 take away 4.*

Look and See

Get 5 red squares.

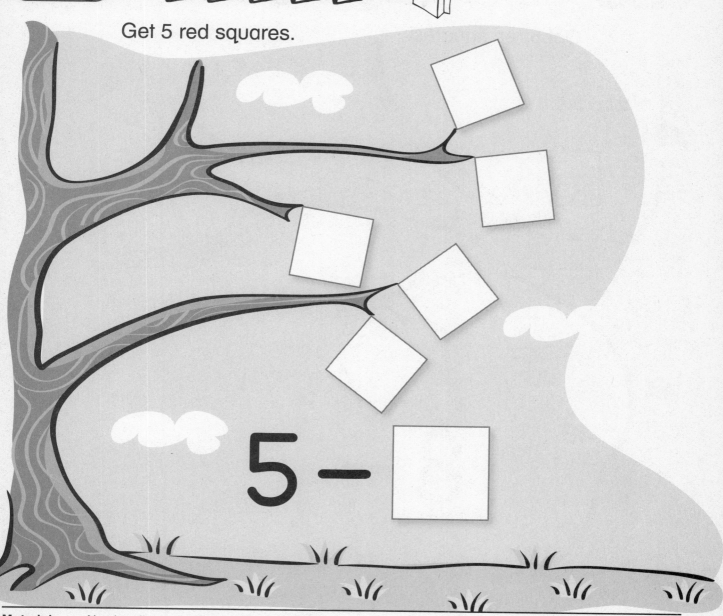

$$5 - \square$$

Materials	Number tiles 1–5, paper bag, 5 red squares
Oral Directions	**TRY** Work together. Put 5 red squares in the empty spaces on the tree. Count them as you put them on the branches. Pretend your squares are leaves. Pick a number tile. Put your tile next to the minus sign. Take that number of leaves off the branches. Put them on the ground. Say: "5 take away ☐ is __," and then trace what you say in the air with your partner. Tell how many leaves are left on the tree. Set the tile aside. Remove the squares. Play until the bag is empty.
	TRY AGAIN Put the tiles back in the bag. Play again!

Look and See

Start 👫 Put ① ② ③ ④ ⑤ ⑥ ⑦ ⑧ in a 🛍.

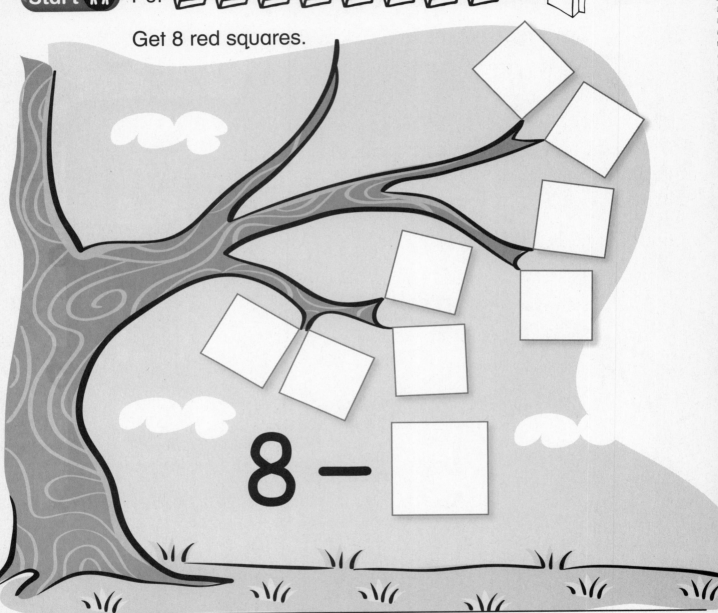

Get 8 red squares.

$$8 - $$

Materials	Number tiles 1–8, paper bag, 8 red squares

Oral Directions

TRY Work together. Put 8 red squares in the spaces on the tree. Count them as you put them on the branches. Pretend your squares are leaves. Pick a number tile. Put your tile next to the minus sign. Take that number of leaves off the branches. Put them on the ground. Say: "8 take away ☐ is __," and then trace what you say in the air with your partner. Tell how many leaves are left on the tree. Set the tile aside. Remove the squares. Play until the bag is empty.

TRY AGAIN Put the tiles back in the bag. Play again!

Name _____

Daily Common
Core Review
7-5

1

Ⓐ 4 − 3

Ⓑ 4 − 1

Ⓒ 3 − 3

Ⓓ 3 − 1

2

Ⓐ 2 and 3 is 5.

Ⓑ 3 and 3 is 6.

Ⓒ 4 and 3 is 7.

Ⓓ 5 and 3 is 8.

3

6 take away 4 is 2.

Directions Have students: **1** mark the subtraction that matches the picture; **2** mark the sentence that tells about adding the groups of squares; **3** mark Xs on the guitars to match the sentence.

Copyright © Pearson Education, Inc., or its affiliates. All Rights Reserved. K

1

8 take away 5 is 3.

$$8 - 5 = 3$$

2

9   take away   3   is   6.

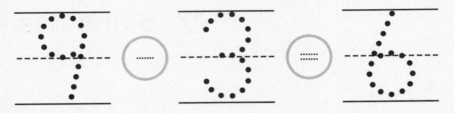

3

5   take away   4   is   1.

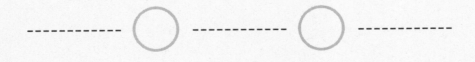

Directions Say: **1** *When you **take away** some objects from a group, you can write an equation to show how many are left. Look at the picture and the subtraction sentence. The sentence tells you how many counters there are in all, how many are taken away, and how many are left. 8 take away 5 is 3 can be written as 8 − 5 = 3. Draw a circle around the number that tells how many were taken away;* **2** *Count the counters and write the number that tells how many on the first line. Look at the subtraction sentence. How many counters are being taken away? Let's mark an X on 3 counters and write 3 on the second line. Draw the minus sign and equal sign to show we are subtracting. Count how many counters are left, and then write that number on the third line.* **3** *Have students use counters to model the problem. Look at the subtraction sentence, mark Xs on the counters to subtract, and then write an equation.* **On the Back!** *Have students draw a picture to show subtracting 7 from 9, and then write an equation.*

Name _____

1

    Ⓐ 2

    Ⓑ 4

    Ⓒ 6

    Ⓓ 8

2

    Ⓐ 10

    Ⓑ 9

    Ⓒ 1

    Ⓓ 0

3

_____

- - - - - - - - - -

_____

_____

- - - - - - - - - -

_____

Directions Have students: **1** mark the number that tells how many crabs in all; **2** mark the number that tells how many eggs are in the nest; **3** draw a group of leaves that is less in number than the group of leaves shown, and then write the numbers that tell how many.

1. ⬤ ⬤ ⬤ ⬤ ⊗ ⊗ ⊗

$$7 - 3 = 4$$

2. ⬤ ⊗ ⊗ ⊗ ⊗ ⊗ ⊗ ⊗ ⊗

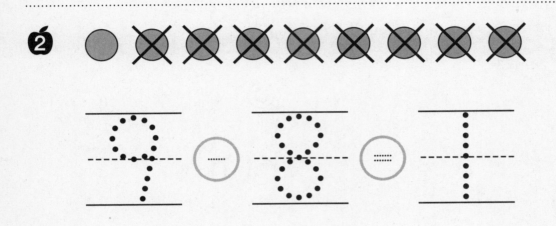

3. ⬤ ⬤ ⬤ ⬤ ⬤ ⬤ ⊗ ⊗

Directions Say: 1. *When you **subtract**, some objects are taken away from a group. These counters show subtraction. How many counters are taken away from the group? So, 3 counters are subtracted from 7 counters. Draw a circle around the number that is being subtracted;* 2. *Look at the picture. How many counters are there in all? How many counters are being subtracted? Write the numbers, the minus sign, and the equal sign to make an equation that tells how many counters are left;* 3. *Write an equation that tells how many counters are left.* **On the Back!** Have students draw a picture to show subtraction, and then write an equation that tells how many are left.

Ⓐ $4 + 4 = 8$ Ⓒ $5 + 3 = 8$

Ⓑ $4 + 5 = 9$ Ⓓ $5 + 5 = 10$

2

Ⓐ 10

Ⓑ 7

Ⓒ 4

Ⓓ 3

3

Directions Have students: **1** mark the equation that matches the picture; **2** mark the number that tells how many flowers are left; **3** use two colors to color the shirts to show one way to make 5.

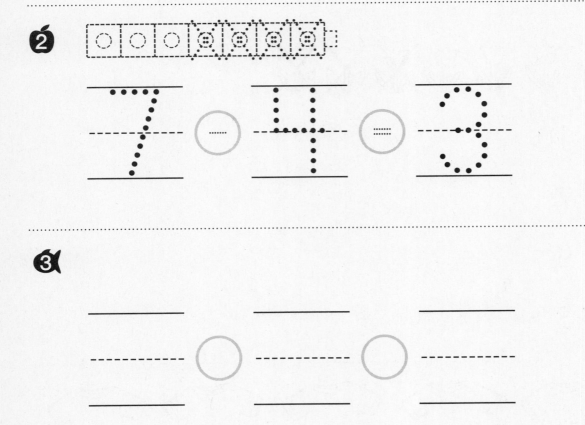

★1

4 ◯ • 2 ◯ _____

      _____

🍎2

7 ◯ 4 ◯ 3

◆3

_____ ◯ _____ ◯ _____
------   ------   ------
_____   _____   _____

Directions Say: ★ *A subtraction equation uses a minus sign to* **subtract** *and an equal sign to show how many are left. Complete the equation that tells how many are left.* 4 − 2 = 2 *is a subtraction equation because it uses the minus sign to subtract and the equal sign to show how many are left;* 🍎 *Listen to this story: There are 7 carrots in a bag. Casey eats 4 carrots. How many carrots are left? You can draw a picture to show what is happening. Draw 7 cubes to show how many there are in all. Mark an X on 4 cubes to show how many are being subtracted. The cubes that are NOT marked with an X tell you how many are left. Write an equation that matches the problem.* ◆ *Have students listen to the story, draw a picture to show what is happening, write an equation, and then explain their work. Say: There are 9 carrots in a bag. Pete eats 6 carrots. How many carrots are left?* **On the Back!** *Have students draw a picture to show what is happening in the equation* 5 − 2 = 3.

1

 2

5 take away 2 is ____.

Ⓐ 7 − 6

Ⓑ 6 − 5

Ⓒ 6 − 1

Ⓓ 5 − 1

Ⓐ 7

Ⓑ 5

Ⓒ 3

Ⓓ 2

 3

Directions Have students: **1** mark the subtraction that matches the picture; **2** mark the number that completes the sentence; **3** draw groups of counters to show two different ways to make 5.

D 7•8

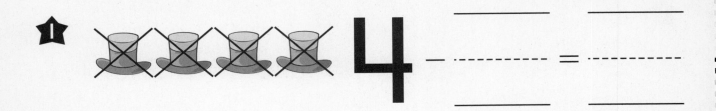

Directions Say: ★ *Look at the rows of hats. We can mark Xs on the hats and write* **equations** *to complete the pattern. Look at the first row. How many hats are there in all? How many hats are marked with an X? How many hats are NOT marked with an X? Complete the equation to match the picture;* ② *Let's look at the next row of hats. How many hats are there in all? Mark an X on 3 hats. How many hats are left? Complete the equation;* ③ *Look at the next row. Let's continue the pattern. How many hats should be marked with an X? How many hats are left? Mark Xs on the hats, and then complete the equation.* ④ *Have students mark Xs to complete the pattern, explain the pattern they see, and then write an equation.* **On the Back!** *Have students write a pattern of equations for 5.*

Listen and Learn

Start 👥 Get ⎡1⎤ ⎡2⎤ ⎡3⎤ ⎡4⎤.

Get 5 red squares.

5 − ☐ = ☐

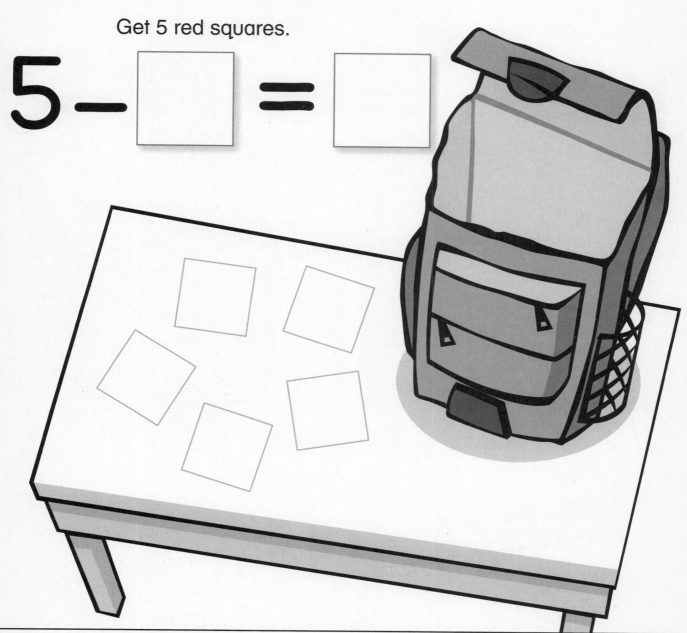

Materials   5 red squares, number tiles 1–4

Oral Directions   **TRY** Pretend your squares are books. Take turns. Put 5 books on the table. Put some, but not all of those books, in the backpack. Put tiles at the top of the page to show what you did. Say, "5 take away ☐ is ☐." Ask your partner to trace what you say in the air. Then say, "The difference is ☐." Ask your partner to repeat what you say.

TRY AGAIN Repeat until each partner gets three or more turns.

Listen and Learn

Start 👫 Get  1 2 3 4 5 6 7 8 9.

Get 10 red squares.

$$10 - \boxed{} = \boxed{}$$

Materials   10 red squares, number tiles 1–9

Oral Directions   **TRY** Pretend your squares are books. Take turns. Put 10 books on the table. Put some, but not all of those books, in the backpack. Put tiles at the top of the page to show what you did. Say, "10 take away ☐ is ☐." Ask your partner to trace what you say in the air. Then say, "The difference is ☐." Ask your partner to repeat what you say.

TRY AGAIN Repeat until each partner gets three or more turns.

Center Game ★★   **7·8**

Ⓐ 3

Ⓑ 4

Ⓒ 5

Ⓓ 6

❷

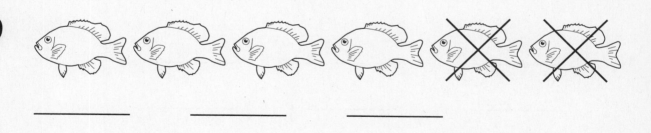

_____   _____   _____

- - - - - - - — - - - - - - = - - - - - -

_____   _____   _____

Directions Have students: ❶ mark the number that tells how many children are in line; ❷ write an equation that matches the picture.

D 7·9

1

$$7 - 3 = 4 \qquad 3 + 4 = 7$$

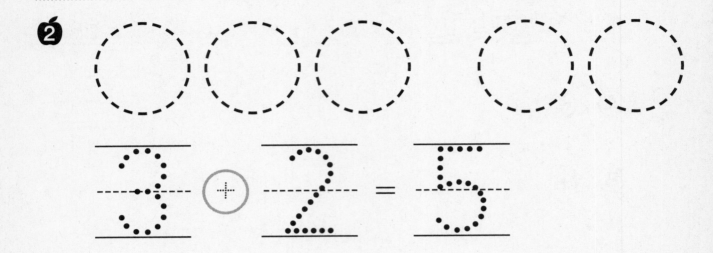 **2**

 3

Directions Say: **1** *Different tools can help you solve problems and write* **equations.** *You have learned that you can write addition equations to add or put together groups. You have also learned that you can write subtraction equations to show taking away. Draw a circle around the subtraction equation. How do you know it is a subtraction equation?* **2** *Let's draw counters to solve a problem. Listen to this story: Loni saw 3 birds at the beach. Later she saw 2 more birds. How many birds did she see in all? Is this an addition or subtraction story? Since you are adding two groups, you will write an addition equation. Do you use a plus sign or a minus sign to write an addition equation? Draw counters and write an equation to match the story. Have students share other tools they could use to solve the problem;* **3** *Listen to the story, use a tool to help solve the problem, and then write the equation. Have students explain whether or not the tool they chose helped to solve the problem. Say: Evan built 6 sand castles. Waves knocked 2 of them down. How many sand castles are left?* **On the Back!** Have students draw a picture that tells an addition or subtraction story, and then write the equation.

Try Together

Start 👥 Get

and 0 1 2 3 4 5 .

Get 5 red squares. Get 5 blue squares.

BOOK STORE

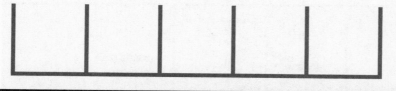

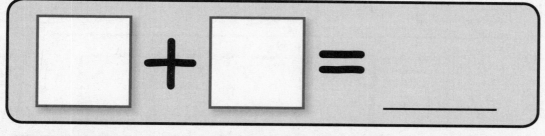

$$\square + \square = \underline{\quad}$$

$$\square - \square = \underline{\quad}$$

Materials   2 sets of number tiles 0–5, 5 red squares, 5 blue squares

Oral Directions   **TRY** Pretend your squares are cars in the bookstore parking lot. Choose 2 number tiles. Act out an addition or subtraction story using your cars and your two numbers. Ask your partner to place the number tiles at the beginning of an equation to match your story. Have your partner finger trace the number that belongs at the end of that equation. Say the equation. Remove the cars from the parking lot. Take turns until each partner gets 5 turns.

TRY AGAIN If you have more time, tell a story about books at the bookstore and ask your partner to tell the matching equation.

Start 👥 Get

and ⟦0⟧⟦1⟧⟦2⟧⟦3⟧⟦4⟧⟦5⟧.

Get 5 red squares. Get 5 blue squares.

Materials   2 sets of number tiles 0–5, 5 red squares, 5 blue squares

Oral Directions   **TRY** Pretend your squares are cars in the toy store parking lot. Choose 2 number tiles. Use them to fill the spaces in the addition equation or in the subtraction equation. Ask your partner to tell a story that has those numbers. Let your partner move cars in the parking lot to act out the story. Have your partner finger trace the number that belongs at the end of the equation. Tell your partner to say the complete equation. Take turns until each partner gets 5 turns.

TRY AGAIN If you have more time, tell your partner an equation. Ask your partner to act out a story about toys at the toy store that matches the equation.

Name _____

⭐**1** 4 − 0 = _____

🍎**2** 0 + 0 = _____

🐦**3** 1 + 2 = _____

❤**4** 0 + 1 = _____

✋**5** 2 + 2 = _____

☕**6** 0 + 5 = _____

🌲**7** 5 − 4 = _____

🏴**8** 3 − 2 = _____

🔷**9** 4 − 1 = _____

🏠**10** 5 − 0 = _____

Directions Have students add or subtract to solve each problem.

Name _____

Topic **8**

©Fluency
Practice/Assessment

1 $2 + 0 =$ _____

2 $3 - 0 =$ _____

3 $0 + 2 =$ _____

4 $1 + 1 =$ _____

5 $2 + 3 =$ _____

6 $3 + 1 =$ _____

7 $4 - 3 =$ _____

8 $5 - 5 =$ _____

9 $5 - 0 =$ _____

10 $4 - 1 =$ _____

Directions Have students add or subtract to solve each problem.

Topic 8 ©**Fluency Practice/Assessment**   **2 of 6**   Copyright © Pearson Education, Inc., or its affiliates. All Rights Reserved. K

1 $1 - 0 =$ _____

2 $0 + 5 =$ _____

3 $1 + 2 =$ _____

4 $1 + 1 =$ _____

5 $3 + 2 =$ _____

6 $4 + 0 =$ _____

7 $3 - 3 =$ _____

8 $5 - 3 =$ _____

9 $3 - 0 =$ _____

10 $5 - 2 =$ _____

Directions Have students add or subtract to solve each problem.

Name _____

⭐**1** 3 + 0 = _____

🍎**2** 0 − 0 = _____

3 1 + 2 = _____

❤**4** 2 + 0 = _____

✋**5** 4 + 1 = _____

☕**6** 1 + 3 = _____

🌲**7** 2 − 1 = _____

🚩**8** 4 − 4 = _____

9 4 − 0 = _____

🏠**10** 5 − 1 = _____

Directions Have students add or subtract to solve each problem.

★1 5 − 0 = _____

🍎2 1 + 0 = _____

🐟3 3 + 0 = _____

♥4 2 + 1 = _____

✋5 0 + 4 = _____

☕6 4 + 1 = _____

🌲7 2 − 2 = _____

🏴8 3 − 1 = _____

◆9 5 − 2 = _____

🏠10 4 − 0 = _____

Directions Have students add or subtract to solve each problem.

⭐**1** $0 + 4 =$ _____

🍎**2** $2 - 0 =$ _____

🐟**3** $0 + 3 =$ _____

💗**4** $1 + 0 =$ _____

✋**5** $5 + 0 =$ _____

☕**6** $2 + 2 =$ _____

🌲**7** $4 - 2 =$ _____

⬛**8** $1 - 1 =$ _____

◆**9** $5 - 1 =$ _____

🏠**10** $3 - 0 =$ _____

Directions Have students add or subtract to solve each problem.

Ruby and Sue Share Flowers

Written by Sophie Paoletti
Illustrated by Jim Steck

Ruby Rabbit has 2 flowers for

Sue Skunk.

Ruby picks 7 more flowers.

Now Ruby has ____ flowers.

Topic 8 • 1

fold down

Sue gives 2 of her flowers

to Ruby.

Sue and Ruby are good pals!

$1 + 2 =$ ____

Now Ruby has ____ flowers.

Topic 8 • 4

Ruby gives 5 of the flowers
to Sue.

Ruby and Sue are good pals!

9 – 5 = _____

Now Ruby has _____ flowers.

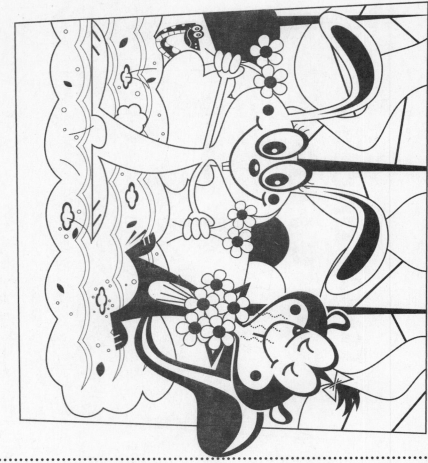

fold up

The two pals meet Sam Snake.

Sam takes 3 flowers and
slides off.

4 – 3 = _____

Now Ruby has _____ flower.

More Addition and Subtraction

Topic 8 Standards
K.OA.A.1, K.OA.A.2, K.OA.A.3, K.OA.A.4, K.OA.A.5
See the front of the Student's Edition for complete standards.

Dear Family,

Your child is continuing to learn about addition and subtraction. In this topic, he or she will learn to compose, or put two numbers together, to make numbers through 10. Your child will also decompose, or take a number apart, to make two numbers with the same total value. In addition, he or she will write addition and subtraction equations.

Making Numbers
There is more than one way to show a number.

$4 = 0 + 4$
$4 = 1 + 3$
$4 = 2 + 2$
$4 = 3 + 1$
$4 = 4 + 0$

The total number is always 4.

Try this activity with your child to continue practicing addition and subtraction.

Story Problems

Help your child make up stories about the following equations:
$6 + 2 = 8$, $7 - 5 = 2$, $8 + 2 = 10$, $6 - 5 = 1$, $4 + 5 = 9$, $9 - 3 = 6$.

Observe Your Child

Focus on Mathematical Practice 7:
Look for and make use of structure.

Help your child become proficient with Mathematical Practice 7. Before your child makes up a story to match the equation, ask how he or she knows the equation is addition or subtraction.

Más sobre la suma y la resta

Estándares del Tema 8

K.OA.A.1, K.OA.A.2, K.OA.A.3, K.OA.A.4, K.OA.A.5
Los estándares completos se encuentran en las lecciones del Libro del estudiante.

Estimada familia:

Su niño(a) continúa aprendiendo sobre la suma y la resta. En este tema, él o ella aprenderá a componer, o juntar dos números, para formar números hasta 10. Su niño(a) también descompondrá, o quitará un número, para formar dos números con el mismo valor total. Además, él o ella escribirá ecuaciones de suma y de resta.

Formar números
Hay más de una manera de mostrar un número.

$4 = 0 + 4$
$4 = 1 + 3$
$4 = 2 + 2$
$4 = 3 + 1$
$4 = 4 + 0$

El número total siempre es 4.

Intente esta actividad con su niño(a) para continuar practicando la suma y la resta.

Problema-cuento

Ayude a su niño(a) a inventar cuentos sobre las ecuaciones siguientes:
$6 + 2 = 8$, $7 - 5 = 2$, $8 + 2 = 10$, $6 - 5 = 1$, $4 + 5 = 9$, $9 - 3 = 6$.

Observar a su niño(a)

Enfoque en la Práctica matemática 8:
Buscar y usar la estructura

Ayude a su niño(a) a adquirir competencia en la Práctica matemática 8. Antes de que su niño(a) invente un cuento que represente la ecuación, pregúntele cómo sabe si la ecuación es una suma o una resta.

Name _____

Recycle

 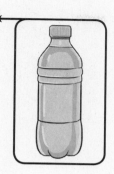

_____   _____   _____

- - - - - - - - ( ) - - - - - - - - = - - - - - - - -

_____   _____   _____

_____   _____   _____

- - - - - - - - ( ) - - - - - - - - = - - - - - - - -

_____   _____   _____

Directions Say: *Aluminum cans and water bottles can be recycled. Recycled aluminum cans can be made into new aluminum cans. Water bottles can be made into car parts and clothing.* ❶ and ❷ Have students decide whether the water bottles show addition or subtraction. Have them make up stories to match the bottles, and then write an equation to tell the related facts. **Extension** Have students draw a picture of aluminum cans, make up stories, and then write an equation to tell the related facts.

Name _____

More Recycling

⭐ 1

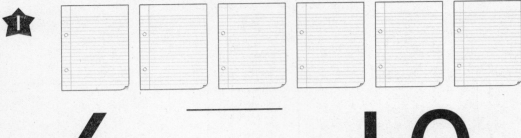

$$6 + \underline{\quad\quad} = 10$$

🍎 2

$$5 + \underline{\quad\quad} = 10$$

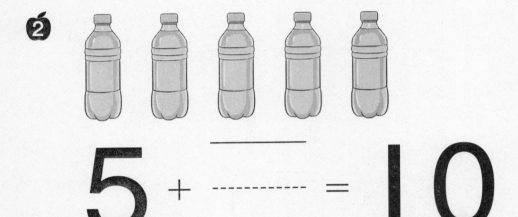

3

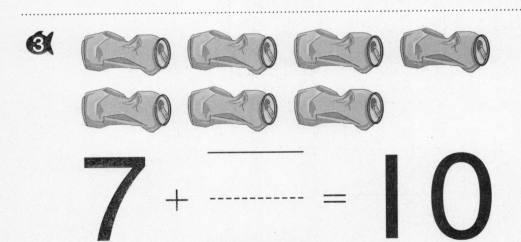

$$7 + \underline{\quad\quad} = 10$$

Directions Say: *Did you know that besides aluminum cans and water bottles you can also recycle paper? Recycled paper is sorted by type, chopped into small pieces, and then made into something new such as paper, greeting cards or paper towels.* ⭐–3 Say: *You can use counters to help you find the missing part of 10.* Have students use counters to find the missing part of 10, draw more pictures to make 10, and then write the missing number to complete the equation. Then have them explain how they know their answer is correct. **Extension** Have students draw a group of water bottles, write the number they drew, and then determine how many more they need to make 10.

1

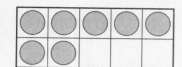

Ⓐ 6

Ⓑ 7

Ⓒ 8

Ⓓ 9

 2

Directions Have students: **1** mark the number that tells how many counters are in the ten-frame; **2** draw a circle around the group of teddy bears that is less in number than the group of teddy bears in the box.

Name _____

⭐ 1

_____ _____

_____ and _____

🍎 2

$4 = 2 + 2$

⭐ 3

$5 = \underline{\quad} + \underline{\quad}$

💜 4

$5 = \underline{\quad} + \underline{\quad}$

Directions ⭐ Say: *We can **break apart** numbers to show subtraction. Let's use the cube train to help us. How many cubes are in the train? Draw a circle around the first 2 cubes, and then draw a circle around the last 3 cubes. This shows one way to break apart 5. How many cubes are in each part? Write the numbers. 2 and 3 is a number pair for 5.* 🍎 Have students use red and yellow counters to help them break apart the group of cats. Say: *Draw a circle around 2 cats, and then draw another circle around the last 2 cats. How many are in each group? This shows one number pair for 4. Write the numbers to complete the equation.* ⭐ and 💜 Have students draw a circle around two groups to show different number pairs for 5, and then complete each equation to show different ways to break apart 5. **On the Back!** Have students draw a group of 4 counters, draw a circle around two groups to show a different way to break apart 4, and then write the number in each group.

Look and See

Start 👫 Put ⏹1 ⏹2 ⏹3 ⏹4 in a .

Get a ✏️ or a ▭.

Materials	Number tiles 1–4, paper bag, pencil or craft stick
Oral Directions	**TRY** Count the starfish. Take turns. Pick a tile from the bag. Count that number of starfish. Put a pencil or a craft stick between the starfish to show that number of starfish in one group. Count the number in each group. Ask your partner to tell the number of starfish in all, and the number of starfish in each group. Play until the bag is empty.
	TRY AGAIN If you have time, play again! This time, trace numbers in the air to show your two parts of 5.

Look and See

Start 👫 Get ⬚1 ⬚2 ⬚3 ⬚4 .

Get a ✏️ or a ▬ .

Materials	Number tiles 1–4, pencil or craft stick
Oral Directions	**TRY** Count the starfish. Take turns. Put a pencil or a craft stick between the starfish to make two groups of starfish. Put a tile next to one group to show the number in that group. Ask your partner to show a tile for the number in the other group. Trace numbers in the air to show your two parts of 5. Play until each partner gets three turns.
	TRY AGAIN If you have time, play again! This time, say your two parts of 5. Ask your partner to say those two parts of 5 in a different order.

Name _____

 ①

Ⓐ 7

Ⓑ 8

Ⓒ 9

Ⓓ 10

🍎 ②

Directions Have students: ① mark the number that tells how many sailboats; ② draw a group of buttons that is greater in number than the group of buttons shown.

Name _____

⭐ 2 + 2 = 4   4 − 2 = 2

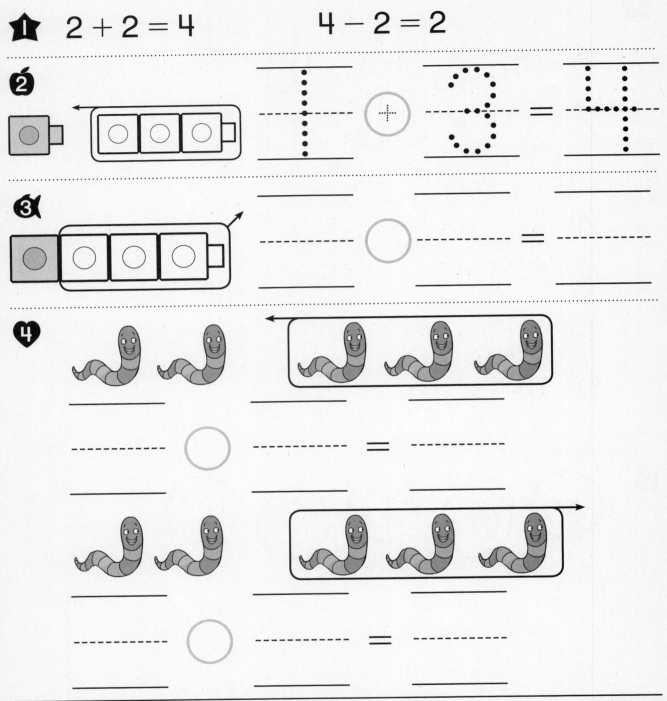

Directions Say: ⭐ *Addition and subtraction are math* **operations.** *How are the equations alike? How are they different? These equations are related facts. Draw a circle around the operation that shows addition. Mark an X on the operation that shows subtraction;* ② *You can use connecting cubes to help you write related facts. Look at the picture. Which operation is shown, addition or subtraction? How do you know? Use cubes to model the addition, and then write an equation to match;* ③ *Use cubes to model the operation shown, and then write an equation to match. This equation and the equation in Item 2 are related facts.* ④ *Have students listen to the story and use connecting cubes to help act out the story to choose an operation. Then have them complete the equations to tell the related facts. Say: 2 worms are in a group. 3 more join them. How many worms are there in all? Then say: 5 worms are in a group. 3 leave the group. How many worms are left?* **On the Back!** *Have students write an addition and related subtraction fact.*

Name ______________________

1

Ⓐ $4 + 4 = 8$

Ⓑ $4 + 5 = 9$

Ⓒ $5 + 4 = 9$

Ⓓ $5 + 5 = 10$

2

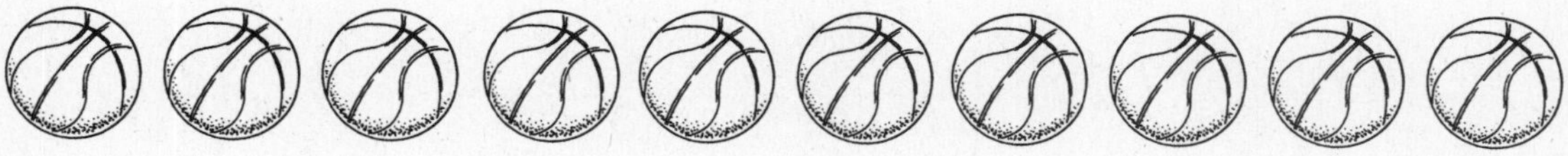

Ⓐ 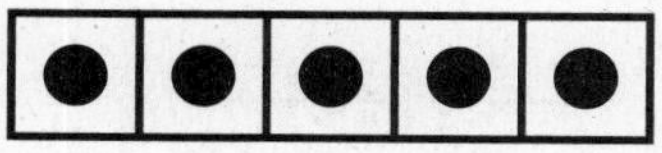

Ⓑ 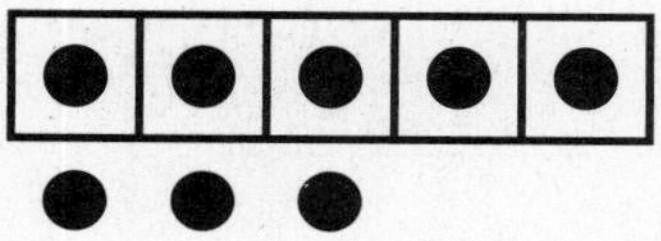

Ⓒ 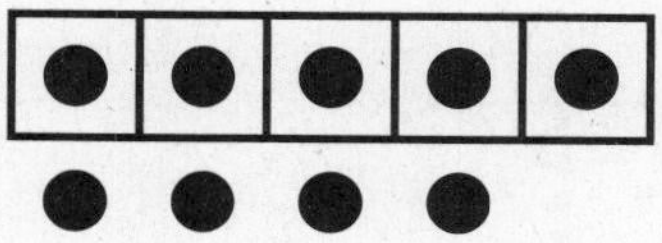

Ⓓ 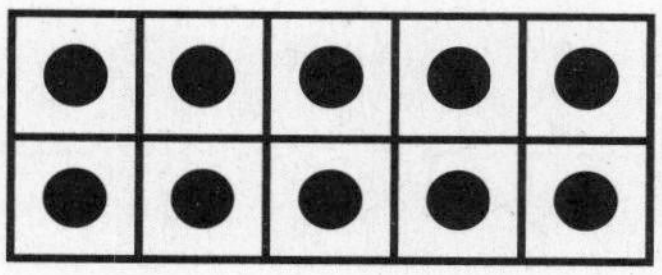

3

Directions Have students: **1** mark the equation that matches the picture; **2** mark the picture that shows how many basketballs; **3** count the toys in each group, and then write the numbers that tell how many of each kind of toy.

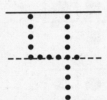 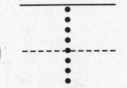

Directions Say: ⭐ *You can tell a story and draw a picture to show how many **in all** or how many are **left**. 4 bunnies play in a field. 1 bunny joins them. How many bunnies are there in all? Draw a picture to solve the problem. How many bunnies play in a field? Draw that number of bunnies in one group. How many bunnies join them? Draw that number in a different group;* ② *Do you need to find how many in all, or how many are left? How do you know? Write an equation to match the picture. What is 4 + 1?* ③ *Have students tell a story for 4 − 1. Have them draw a picture to illustrate their story, and then write the equation to match.* **On the Back!** *Have students draw a picture for 1 + 2 = 3, and then tell a friend a story for the drawing.*

Look and See

Start 🏃🏃 Put 1 2 3 4 5 in a 🛍.

Get a ✏.

Materials   Number tiles 1–5, paper bag, paper and pencil

Oral Directions

TRY Take turns. Pick a tile from the bag. Tell an addition or a subtraction story using that number and something you see at the beach like swimmers, sand castles, and birds. Draw a picture of your story on another piece of paper.

TRY AGAIN If you have time, play again! This time tell stories with different things you see at the beach.

 # Look and See

Partner Talk

Share your thinking while you work.

Start 👫 Put [1] [2] [3] [4] [5] in a 🛍.

Get a ✏️.

Materials	Number tiles 1–5, paper bag, paper and pencil
Oral Directions	**TRY** Take turns. Pick a tile from the bag. Tell an addition or a subtraction story using that number and something you see at the beach like swimmers, sand castles, and birds. Draw a picture of your story on another piece of paper. Write an addition or subtraction equation to match your picture.
	TRY AGAIN If you have time, play again! This time tell stories with different things you see at the beach.

Center Game ★★ **8·3**

Name _____

1

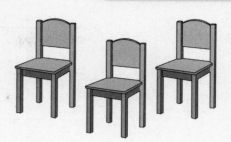

Ⓐ $4 + 3 = 7$

Ⓑ $5 + 2 = 7$

Ⓒ $4 + 4 = 8$

Ⓓ $5 + 3 = 8$

2

Directions Have students: **1** mark the equation that matches the picture; **2** draw a group of flowers that is less in number than the group of flowers shown in the box.

Name _____

 ★ 1

⎯⎯⎯⎯

- - - - - - - - -

$4 - 3 =$ ⎯⎯⎯⎯

❷ $3 + 2 =$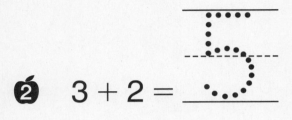

⎯⎯⎯⎯

- - - - - - - - -

❸ $5 - 1 =$ ⎯⎯⎯⎯

⎯⎯⎯⎯

- - - - - - - - -

❹ $3 - 3 =$ ⎯⎯⎯⎯

⎯⎯⎯⎯

- - - - - - - - -

✋ 5 $2 + 1 =$ ⎯⎯⎯⎯

Directions Say: ★ *You can choose different ways to solve an **equation**. Look at the subtraction problem. Let's draw a picture to solve this equation. Draw 4 marbles to show how many there are in all. How many marbles are taken away? Mark an X on that number of marbles. How many are left? Write the number to complete the equation.* Have students share other ways to solve the problem; ❷ *Look at the addition problem. Let's count on to solve the problem. Start at 3 and count two more: 3 … 4, 5.* Have students share other ways to solve the problem. ❸–✋ Have students solve the equation any way they choose, and then tell how they solved the problem. **On the Back!** Have students write an addition problem, and then choose two different ways to solve it.

Math in Motion

Partner Talk

Share your thinking while you work.

Start 👥 Put 4 5 in a 🛍️.

4

5

TAP
TAP

Materials   Number tiles 4–5, a bag for the tiles

Oral Directions   **TRY** Tap your left foot on the floor four times. Tap your right foot on the floor four times. Tap your left foot on the floor five times. Tap your right foot on the floor five times. Take turns. Pick a tile. If you pick 4, choose a way to make 4 by tapping part of 4 with one foot and part of 4 with the other foot. Point to the way you chose on the activity page. Tap your way to make 4. Ask your partner to tap your way to make 4. If you pick 5, choose a way to make 5 by tapping part of 5 with one foot and part of 5 with the other foot. Point to the way you chose on the activity page. Tap your way to make 5. Ask your partner to tap your way to make 5. Put the tile back in the bag. Repeat until each partner picks a tile four times.

TRY AGAIN If you have time, begin again! This time, after you tap your number, ask your partner to tap the same number in a different way.

Math in Motion

Start 👥 Put ⅘ 5️⃣ in a 🛍️.

4

5

Materials	Number tiles 4–5, a bag for the tiles
Oral Directions	**TRY** Tap your feet on the floor to show all the ways to make 4, and then all the ways to make 5. Let your partner show all the ways to make 4, and all the ways to make 5. Then take turns. On your turn, pick a tile. Point to a way to tap that number on the activity page. Tap your feet that way. Ask your partner to make that number by tapping in a different way. Put the tile back in the bag. Repeat until each partner picks a tile four times.
	TRY AGAIN If you have time, begin again! This time, make up a dance to help your class remember the parts of 4 or the parts of 5.

Ⓐ 2   Ⓒ 5

Ⓑ 3   Ⓓ 8

2

 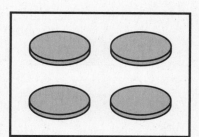

Ⓐ 2 + 3 = 5   Ⓒ 1 + 3 = 4

Ⓑ 0 + 5 = 5   Ⓓ 1 + 4 = 5

3

   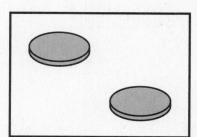

_____   _____   _____

----------- + ---------- = -----------

_____   _____   _____

Directions Have students: **1** mark the number that tells how many white cubes are in the cube train; **2** mark the equation that matches the picture; **3** write an equation that tells how many counters in all.

Name _____

⭐ 1

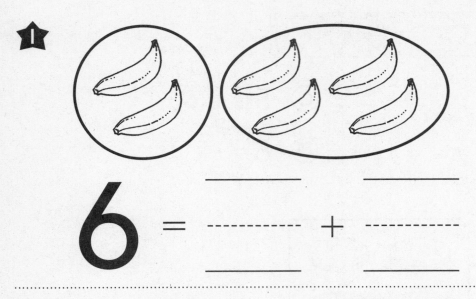

$6 = \underline{\hspace{2cm}} + \underline{\hspace{2cm}}$

🍎 2

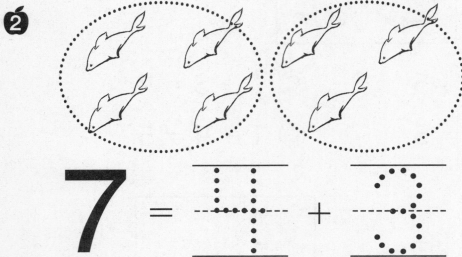

$7 = \underline{4} + \underline{3}$

⭐ 3

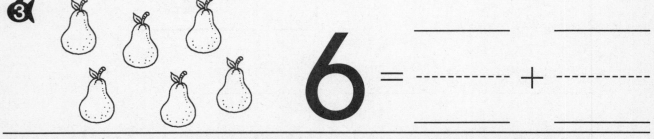

$6 = \underline{\hspace{2cm}} + \underline{\hspace{2cm}}$

Directions Say: ⭐ *You can use counters to* **break apart** *a group of objects and show the number pair. Look at the group of bananas. There are 6 in all. How many bananas are in the first group? Show that many red counters. How many are in the second group? Show that many yellow counters. Count how many in each group, and then write the number pair for 6 to complete the equation;* 🍎 *Use red and yellow counters to show how many whales in all. Let's break apart the group of counters to show a number pair for 7. Show 4 red counters and 3 yellow counters. Draw a circle around the whales to show the two groups. Count how many in each group, and then write the number pair for 7 to complete the equation.* ⭐ Have students use red and yellow counters to show how to break apart the pears, draw a circle around two groups to show a number pair for 6, and then complete the equation to tell the way to break apart 6.

Name _____

 $5 = 4 + 1$

Ⓐ

Ⓒ

Ⓑ

Ⓓ

_____   _____   _____

----------- = ----------- + -----------

_____   _____   _____

Directions Have students: mark the picture that shows the equation $5 = 4 + 1$; ② write an equation that matches the picture; ③ draw a group of counters that is equal in number to the group of counters shown.

1

$$8 = \underline{} + \underline{}$$

2

$$8 = 6 + 2$$

3

$$9 = \underline{} + \underline{}$$

Directions Say: **1** *When you **break apart** a number, you are breaking it into smaller parts. You can use pictures to show a number pair for 8. Color some strawberries red and some strawberries green. How many strawberries are red? How many are green? Write the numbers to complete the equation. This shows one way to break apart 8;* **2** *How many strawberries are there in all? Draw a circle around the two groups of strawberries to show a number pair for 8. How many are in the first group? How many are in the second group? Complete the equation to tell another way to break apart 8.* **3** Have students use red and yellow counters to show how to break apart the 9 strawberries, draw a circle around two groups of strawberries to show a number pair for 9, and then complete the equation to show a way to break apart 9. **On the Back!** Have students draw a group of 9 objects, draw a circle around two groups to show a different way to break apart 9, and then write the number pair.

Look and See

Partner Talk
Share your thinking while you work.

Start 👥 Put 1 2 3 4 5 6 7 8 in a 🛍.

Get a ✏️ or a ▬.

Materials Number tiles 1–8, a bag for the tiles, a pencil or a craft stick

Oral Directions **TRY** Count the shells. Ask your partner to count the clouds. Take turns. Pick a tile from the bag. Count that number of clouds. Put a pencil or a craft stick between the clouds to show that number of clouds in one group. Ask your partner to say the number of clouds in all, and then the number in each group. Repeat for the shells. Take turns until the bag is empty.

TRY AGAIN If you have time, begin again! This time, trace numbers in the air to show your two parts of 8 or your two parts of 9.

Look and See

Start 👥 Get  1 2 3 4 4 5 6 7 8.

Get a ✏️ or a ▬.

Materials   Number tiles 1, 2, 3, 4, 4, 5, 6, 7, 8; a bag for the tiles, a pencil or a craft stick

Oral Directions   **TRY** Count the number of clouds. Ask your partner to count the shells. Take turns. Choose clouds or shells. Put a pencil or a craft stick between the shells or the clouds to make two groups. Put a tile next to one group to show the number in that group. Ask your partner to show a tile for the number in the other group. Trace the numbers in the air to show your two parts of 8 or your two parts of 9. Take turns until each partner gets three turns.

TRY AGAIN If you have time, begin again! This time, say your two parts of 8 or your two parts of 9. Ask your partner to say those two parts of 8 or 9 in a different order.

Name _____

 1

 (A) $6 + 2 = 8$ (C) $2 + 6 = 8$

 (B) $6 - 2 = 4$ (D) $4 + 2 = 6$

 2

 (A) $5 = 2 + 3$ (C) $9 = 4 + 5$

 (B) $9 = 7 + 2$ (D) $8 = 4 + 4$

 3

Directions Have students: ★ mark the equation that shows subtraction; ② mark the equation that describes the picture; ③ draw a group of squares that is less in number than the group of squares shown.

⭐ $4 \oplus 2 = 6$ $4 \ominus 2 = 2$

🍎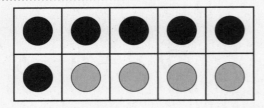

$10 = 6 + 4$

❸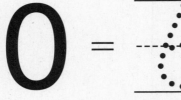

$10 =$ _____ + _____

💙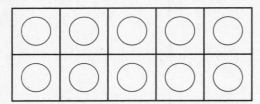

$10 =$ _____ + _____

Directions Say: ⭐ *Addition and subtraction are types of* **operations.** *Draw a circle around the equation that shows addition and mark an X on the equation that shows subtraction;* 🍎 *You can use counters and a ten-frame to break apart 10 and show the number pair. Look at the ten-frame. How many spaces are in a ten-frame? How many counters are black? How many are gray? This shows one way to break apart 10. Write the number pair to complete the equation.* ❸ *and* 💙 *Have students color the counters in the ten-frame red and yellow to show a number pair for 10, and then complete the equation to tell the way to break apart 10.* **On the Back!** *Have students draw 10 counters, draw a circle around two groups to show a different way to break apart 10, and then write the number in each group.*

Look and See

Start 👫 Put ① ② ③ ④ ⑤ ⑥ ⑦ ⑧ ⑨ in a 🛍.

Get a ✏️ or a ▬ .

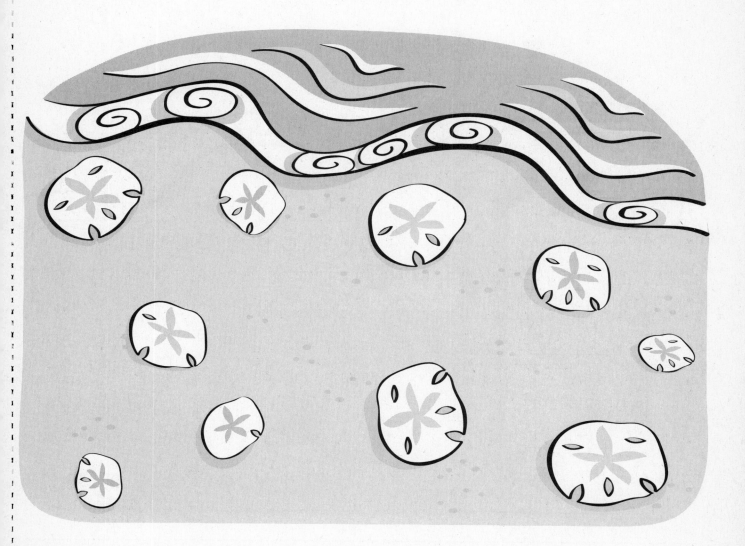

Materials	Number tiles 1–9, a bag for the tiles, a pencil or a craft stick
Oral Directions	**TRY** Count the sand dollars. Take turns. Pick a tile from the bag. Count that number of sand dollars. Put a pencil or a craft stick between the sand dollars to show that number of sand dollars in one group. Count the number of sand dollars in the other group. Ask your partner to tell the number of sand dollars in all, and the number of sand dollars in each group. Play until the bag is empty.
	TRY AGAIN If you have time, play again! This time, trace numbers in the air to show your two parts of 10.

Center Game ★ 8·7

Look and See

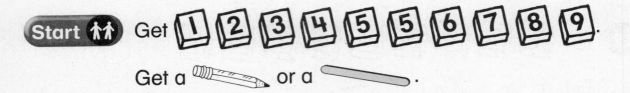

Start 👫 Get ⬚1 ⬚2 ⬚3 ⬚4 ⬚5 ⬚5 ⬚6 ⬚7 ⬚8 ⬚9.

Get a ✏️ or a ▬ .

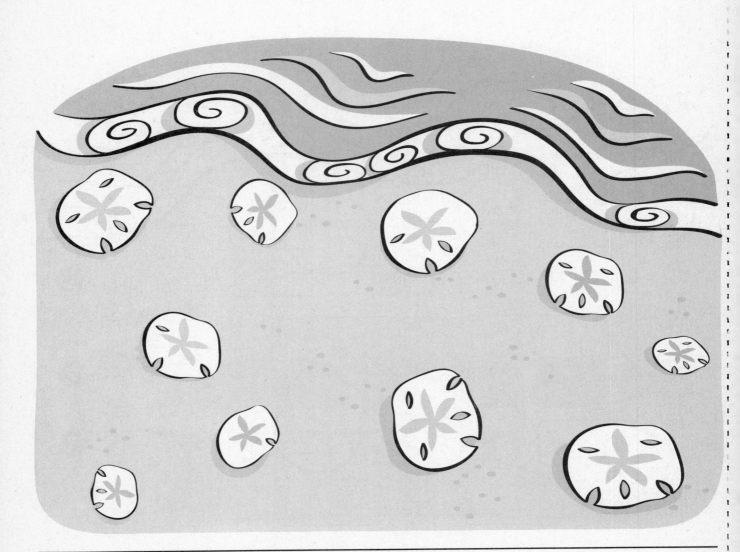

Materials   Number tiles 1, 2, 3, 4, 5, 5, 6, 7, 8, 9; a pencil or a craft stick

Oral Directions   **TRY** Count the sand dollars. Take turns. Put a pencil or a craft stick between the sand dollars to make two groups of sand dollars. Put a tile next to one group to show the number in that group. Ask your partner to show a tile for the number in the other group. Trace numbers in the air to show your two parts of 10. Play until each partner gets three turns.

TRY AGAIN If you have time, play again! This time, say your two parts of 10. Ask your partner to say those two parts of 10 in a different order.

Center Game ★★ **8·7**   K

Name _____

⭐ 1

Ⓐ

Ⓑ

Ⓒ

Ⓓ

 2

$7 = $ _____ _____

_____ + _____

_____ _____

Directions Have students: ⭐ mark the picture that shows 9 carrots; 🍎 draw a circle around two groups of cherries to show a number pair for 7, and then complete the equation to tell one way to break apart 7.

⭐ 1

$$10 = \underline{\quad\quad} + \underline{\quad\quad}$$

🍎 2

$$9 = 3 + 6$$

⭐ 3

$$7 = \underline{\quad\quad} + \underline{\quad\quad}$$

Directions Say: ⭐ You can use counters to **break apart** 10 and show the number pair. Look at the ten-frame. Color some counters red and some counters yellow. How many are red? How many are yellow? Write the number pair to complete the equation and show one way to break apart 10; 🍎 Listen to this story: Nicholas has 9 marbles. He wants to give some of them to Jason and some of them to Matt. How can he break apart the group of marbles? How many marbles does Nicholas have in all? Draw a circle around 3 marbles to show how many he could give to Jason. How many are left? Draw a circle around the marbles to show how many he could give to Matt. Complete the equation to show how many in each group. ⭐ Have students listen to the story, draw a circle around two groups to show breaking apart, and then complete the equation to match the groups. Have them explain how they know their answer is correct. Say: *Megan has 7 beach balls. She wants to give some to Mia and some to Drew. How can she break apart the group of beach balls?* **On the Back!** Have students draw 5 toys, draw a circle around two groups to show a way to break apart 5, and then write the number in each group.

Name _____

 1

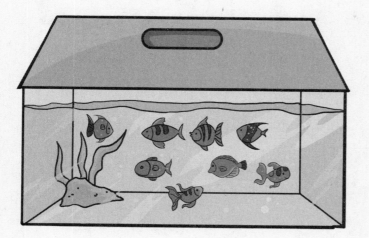

Ⓐ 7

Ⓑ 8

Ⓒ 9

Ⓓ 10

 2

Directions Have students: ⭐ mark the number that tells how many fish are in the fish tank; ② draw a circle around the group that shows more apples than the group shown on the plate.

D 8·9

1 $5 + 2 = 7$

2 $8 + 2 = 10$

3 $6 + \underline{\quad} = 10$

4 $1 + \underline{\quad} = 10$

Directions Say: **1** *There are 7 plums in all. There are 5 plums inside the basket and 2 plums outside of the basket. You can write an* **equation** *to show how many plums in all, and how many in each part. Draw a circle around the numbers that tell the parts in red and the number that tells the sum in blue;* **2** *You can use cubes to help find the missing part of 10. Look at the 10-cube train. Some of the cubes are covered. Let's find how many are covered to complete the equation. Use blue cubes to show how many cubes are NOT covered. How many cubes are NOT covered? Use red cubes and count on to find how many cubes are covered: 9, 10. How many red cubes are covered? Write the missing number in the equation to tell the parts of 10.* **3** – **4** *Have students count the cubes to find one part of 10, use red cubes to find how many are covered, and then write the missing number in the equation to tell the parts of 10.* **On the Back!** *Have students draw pictures to show parts of 10, and then write an equation to match the picture.*

Helping Hands

Partner Talk

Share your thinking while you work.

Start 👥 Put |1| |2| |3| |4| |5| in a 🛍.

Get |5| |6| |7| |8| |9|.

Get 10 red squares. Get 10 blue squares.

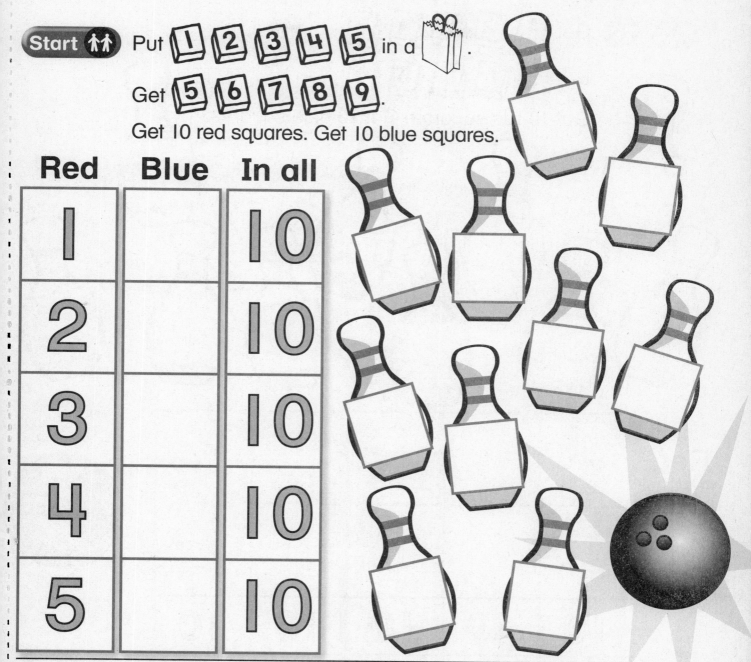

Red	Blue	In all
1		10
2		10
3		10
4		10
5		10

Materials   Number tiles 1–5 and 5–9, paper bag, 10 red squares, 10 blue squares

Oral Directions   **TRY** Put the number tiles with 1, 2, 3, 4, and 5 in a bag. Take turns. Pick a tile from the bag. Put that number of red squares on the bowling pins. Use the tile to cover that number. Ask your partner to cover the other bowling pins with blue squares. Then, have your partner count the number of blue squares. Then have your partner find a number tile to show the number of blue squares and put that number tile next to yours. Take turns until you have used all of the tiles.

TRY AGAIN If you have more time, remove the tiles. Put the 1–5 tiles back in the bag. Play again! This time, when you are done, say all the ways to make 10.

Helping Hands

Start 👫 Get ⬜1⬜ ⬜2⬜ ⬜3⬜ ⬜4⬜ ⬜5⬜.

Put ⬜5⬜ ⬜6⬜ ⬜7⬜ ⬜8⬜ ⬜9⬜ in a 🛍.

Get 10 red squares. Get 10 blue squares.

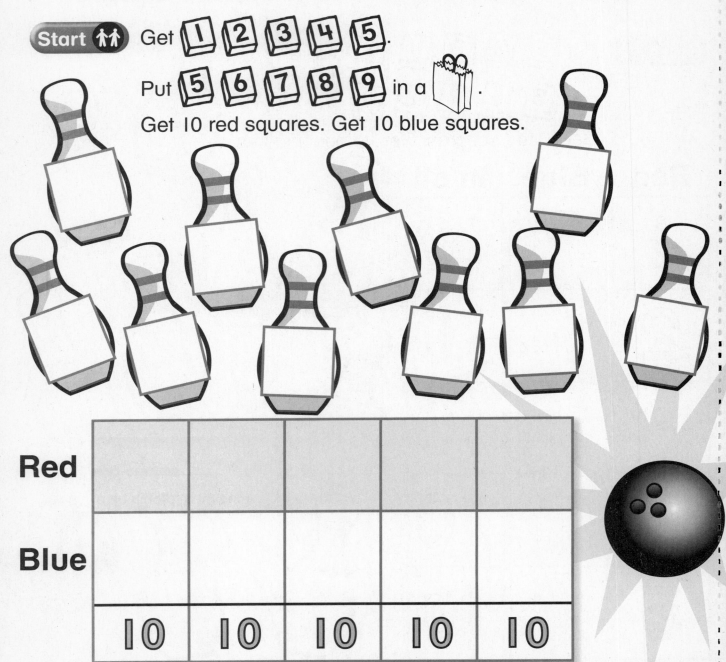

Red					
Blue					
	10	10	10	10	10

Materials Number tiles 1–5 and 5–9, paper bag, 10 red squares, 10 blue squares

Oral Directions **TRY** Put the number tiles with 1, 2, 3, 4, and 5 in the gray spaces. Put 2 in the first gray space, then 5, then 1, then 4, and then 3 in the last gray space. Put the number tiles with 5, 6, 7, 8, and 9 in a bag. Take turns. Pick a tile from the bag. Put that number tile where it belongs to make 10 in all. Put some red squares and some blue squares on the bowling pins to show the two parts of 10 that you made. Take turns until you have used all of the tiles.

TRY AGAIN If you have time, remove the tiles from the white spaces. Put them back in the bag. Play again! This time, when you are done, say all the ways to make 10.

Name _____

⭐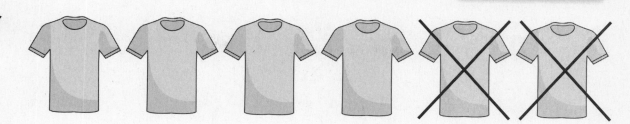

Ⓐ $7 - 2 = 5$

Ⓑ $6 - 4 = 2$

Ⓒ $6 - 2 = 4$

Ⓓ $4 - 2 = 2$

❷

_____   _____   _____

- - - - - - - — - - - - - - - = - - - - - - -

_____   _____   _____

Directions Have students: ⭐ mark the equation that matches the picture; ❷ write an equation that matches the picture.

Name _____

⭐ $8 = 6 + 2$

....

② 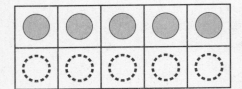 $5 + 5 = 10$

③ 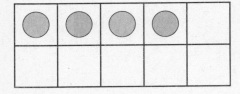 $4 + \underline{} = 10$

④ 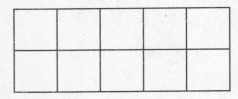 $3 + \underline{} = 10$

Directions Say: ⭐ *In an addition equation, the **sum** tells how many in all. Draw a circle around the sum in the equation;*
② *Look at the equation. One of the parts of 10 is missing. You can use a ten-frame to help find the missing number. How
many spaces are in the ten-frame? How many counters are in the ten-frame now? Let's draw counters to find the missing
part of 10. What is the missing number? Write the missing number to complete the equation;* ③ *How many counters
are in the ten-frame? Draw counters to find the missing part of 10. How many counters did you draw? Write the missing
number in the equation.* ④ Have students draw red counters in the ten-frame to show the part that they know, draw
yellow counters in the empty spaces in the ten-frame and count to find the missing part of 10, and then write the missing
number in the equation. **On the Back!** Have students draw 10 circles. Have them color up to 9 circles red, and then write
an equation for a partner to solve. The partner should find the missing part of 10.